8 - 1.2

THE
FRIENDLY STORY
CARAVAN

THE
FRIENDLY STORY
CARAVAN

Compiled and Edited by

ANNA PETTIT BROOMELL

With an Introduction by
DOROTHY CANFIELD FISHER

J. B. Lippincott Company

PHILADELPHIA AND NEW YORK

INTRODUCTION

BY DOROTHY CANFIELD FISHER

WHY DO people like Quaker stories? Not only members of the Society of Friends, or of the Wider Quaker Fellowship, or friends of Friends. By buying for their children year after year, one edition after another of these Quaker stories the readers of the general public, often accused of caring only for sentimentality or for brutal sensationalism, have conclusively proved that they are looking for something of more spiritual worth. When they find it, they obviously like and value it.

Probably every observer of the American scene would have his own idea of the reason for the phenomenon—surprising in the publishing world—of the continuous sale on the open market of these stories. Here is mine: in our days, as never before, humanity is on trial, with the verdict undecided. The appalling events of our times have been poured over our minds like chemicals poured over exposed photographic film. They have brought out images of wrong-doings and idiocies of which we did not dream, which we cannot, now, banish from our awareness.

But it is axiomatic of humanity: men and women are rooted in the need to hope. We no longer have a confident faith in the worthwhileness of our race, but we still hope for it. Men and women are hungering and thirsting for some evidence—real evidence, not wish-thinking illusions—that the righteousness we all know does exist in human hearts is strong enough to cope with evil. Our religious leaders, philosophers, thinkers, seers have always told us that the potential power of the spirit is greater than materialism. Sick at heart, we look anxiously everywhere for proof that they are right.

Above all we long with a passion that is like a remorse for proof to give our children that their older generation has not brought them into a world which is helpless before wrong-doing. And here, ready to our need, are the Quakers with these stories for young people.

But we would not feel the impact of the substance in these stories if the Friends did not have a gift all their own for telling them. It is not preeminently a literary gift. Their great gift, their unique gift is this: they speak naturally of goodness. *Naturally*.

To be able to speak, and to act naturally is an inimitable priceless skill. It cannot be improvised rapidly by wishing to do so on some special occasion. Nor can the ability to speak naturally of the life of the spirit be had for nothing. The Friends have paid for it. With austere certainty of purpose they have resisted in their lives, in their religion, the trend, so familiar to us all, of *setting apart from everyday human life* the attempt to practise goodness, by special circumstance, special rites (beautiful though they may be), special ornamentation and tradition. They made their choice generations ago. They would rather be able to speak naturally of goodness than eloquently.

If there is one faculty which children have, it is knowing by intuition when people are speaking to them with total sincerity of meaning, or with half-aware reservations. When children turn on an older speaker that life-and-death look of inquiry, what they see is the total personality of the speaker, rather than his words at that instant. The Quakers have made many sacrifices of pleasing qualities highly prized by others, to make and keep their total personalities such as to bear this scrutiny from youth.

Most of us cannot, when we talk of goodness, command our voices to those taken-for-granted, unaffectedly real intonations we use when speaking of matters we truly, wholly consider essential to human life. We can say, naturally, convinced and convincing, "Don't lean too far over the rail of the bridge. You'll fall into the river if you do." But we cannot use the same natural intonation in saying "Don't be violent and selfish. Be kind and forgiving." The Quakers can.

We know, as yet, so little about the complexities of human behavior, that we do not understand all that is involved in this matter. But we can make a guess that the tap-root out of which blooms the serene flower of Friendly sincerity, with its not-to-be-imitated power to convince, is that their conception of goodness is all-inclusive. They have no silent reservations, no half-acknowledgments, no qualifications. They do not say that goodness would be better if based on a theory of life identical to their own. Goodness is goodness, no matter where or in whom it is found. Like the waters of the earth flowing into the spacious oneness of the ocean, their idea of what goodness is carries them along by a law of spiritual gravity, till it includes every son or daughter of Man.

They do not say this in words. We may not be consciously aware of it. But longing as we are in our troubled days, for human unity, it may be that our realization of it explains why we want our young people to have a contact with Friends through these simply told stories of the triumph of good over evil in actual human lives.

FOREWORD
BY THE AUTHOR

THE RELATION between *The Friendly Story Caravan* and its predecessors, *The Children's Story Garden* and *The Children's Story Caravan* is not easy to state. This third volume is not a sequel, because a little more than half of the material has been drawn from the earlier collections. Yet it cannot be thought of as a reprint, since the process of selection and addition has made it a new book. While following closely the pattern of the former collections, the new stories are expressed in terms of the present day.

All three books have attempted to teach ethical principles through the telling of stories. These stories were frequently derived from Quaker sources although the principles they illustrate represent the simple virtues which lie behind all human progress and Christian living.

It is hoped that the stories included in this collection will not leave the impression that virtue is always promptly rewarded. The editor searched in vain for stories which would make clear that the immediate result of non-violence is often prison, seeming defeat or death. She attempted to write several such stories, but the compression of the short story made the sacrifice loom as an end in itself rather than the means to the overcoming of evil. The formula is the same whether the immediate result is success or defeat: Living close to God, people become "tender." Faced with suffering and injustice, "tender" people feel uncomfortable. Feeling uncomfortable, they try to do something about it.

The *Garden* and the *Caravan* have made an astonishing number of friends. In retiring these two books and substituting another, the editor realizes that some people will feel a personal grievance due to the omission of this or that particular story. With these the editor has great sympathy because she has had to sacrifice some of her own favorites. But, since selection had to be made, it was necessary to set up certain criteria. The stories were to be suitable for children over ten years. That eliminated a host of favorites. They were to form a homogeneous collection. Out went saints, ballads, folk tales. THE LION MAKERS from the *Panchatantra,* the oldest story in either collection, was retained because it bears a striking relevancy to our newest problem, the atom bomb. Other considerations which were taken into account were the number of requests which had been received to reprint a given story and the subject matter which would contribute to the greatest variety.

The stories reprinted from *The Children's Story Garden* are: ADVERTISING FOR A THIEF, A RIDE TOWARD WAR PAINT, THE WATER BARREL, THE CHISELED FACE, OUR WORD IS OUR KEEPER, THE WHITE FEATHER, THE LATCH STRING, THE SACRED FLAME, THE SILVER TANKARD, THE HIGHWAYMAN, THE INVINCIBLE LEADER, THE SERMON IN THE WILDERNESS, and NOT LOST BUT GONE BEFORE.

The stories reprinted from *The Children's Story Caravan* are: AN ILL WIND, WHERE LOVE IS THERE GOD IS ALSO, THE WORD OF A GENTLEMAN, THE SILVER PESO, THE ROAD TO CANADA, JANE ADDAMS'S BURGLARS, THE SEVEN KINGDOMS AND THE HIDDEN SPRING, WHO IS MY NEIGHBOR?, PEACEFUL SOLDIERS, THE OLD LADY OF PURCHASE, THE LION-MAKERS, THE SQUIRE'S HALF CROWN, DAVID ALLEN—QUAKER, FAINT HEART FAILED, HOW MUCH LAND DOES A MAN NEED?, and THE BISHOP'S CHAIRS.

Many of the stories in this collection were the result of the collaboration of several people, a collaboration so close that the authors themselves could not say who was responsible for the final draft. Even the stories which the editor wrote did not seem to warrant a signature since the story, in a sense, wrote itself from the facts or folk lore on which it was based. So it was decided to sign only those stories which were contributed by a single author. To those whose names are signed and to those who contributed anonymously, the editor expresses grateful appreciation.

CONTENTS

CONTENTS

THE
FRIENDLY STORY
CARAVAN

WHEN GANDHI CAME

"Is THAT all we have to do, Mother? Gandhiji's train will be coming soon; we must get there early or we won't be able to see him."

Dhan hung a goat skin filled with water on the wall of the mud hut and looked at his mother anxiously, fearing that she might have something more for him to do. His little brother Sudhir did the same with his goat skin. It was heavy for a small boy of ten years, and the muscles bulged on his thin brown body as he lifted it up to the hook. The boys' bodies were shiny with perspiration, for the August day was hot in India. Neither of them wore any clothes except a loin cloth.

"Yes, you may go," his mother said. Dhan knew from the reluctant tone of her voice that there was much more for the two brothers to do. There was cow dung to be gathered for fuel. The boys would follow the cows and pick up the droppings and roll them into patties which were later used for fuel to cook with.

His mother turned back to the kettle of rice boiling over the fire which burned on the floor in one corner of the room.

"Your father will be coming soon. He must eat. I cannot go—I'll never see our beloved Gandhiji, not even in the next incarnation, though I might be closer to him there," she said as if to herself. Then she added, "but you must go, yes you must—this is my work." She sighed and her great, dark eyes rested on the boys for a moment.

The room was bare and ugly and the dim light coming through the windows shone softly on the smaller children squatting on mats on the floor. The baby lay naked, kicking his legs in the air.

3

Their mother was always working, cooking, washing, but Dhan usually didn't think about it at all. In his world all women worked all of the time. It was woman's life. But now when she sighed, Dhan felt a twinge of sadness that she couldn't come too. He loved his mother. Once in a while when she had time to go out and be with her friends, she would laugh and be happy, and then they would all laugh when she came home for she had funny things to tell them; but most of the time she didn't say anything and hardly smiled.

"Rashid pushed in ahead of me at the pump," Dhan said, making a face. "He's a dirty Muslim. I hate him. He wasn't fair. I pushed him too, but he's bigger. Everybody laughed at me. All the dirty Muslims were there."

"Don't talk like that, Dhan," his mother said. "You're going to see Gandhiji. He's a Hindu like us but he loves the Muslims; he loves everyone, Hindus and Muslims— that's what he's coming here for—to ask us to love each other. Governor Casey has urged him to come and stop the fighting and the street brawls."

"Can't we go, Mother?" Dhan said. He didn't want to love the Muslims, all he wanted now was to run to the station with thousands of other people to see Gandhi.

"Yes, yes, go," she said again. She drew her sari about her and stood up and motioned him away, then turned from him to one of the smaller children who had made the baby cry.

"Come on then, Sudhir, we must hurry."

Dhan grabbed his brother's hand. They ran out of the dark mud hut and into the hot sun. Their bare feet padded on the hard dry dirt. On either side of the path there were hundreds of houses just like theirs. This was the bustee area, where the very poor people lived, in the city of Calcutta in India. They had one-room houses filled with children, and the streets swarmed with people day and night. Dhan had never known anything but close-pressing life about him. If he had gone up into the hills or even to a country village he would have been lonely.

They came out onto the streets of Calcutta where there were cars and bullock carts and rickshas drawn by men with thin bodies. Sometimes they passed a cow nosing its way along. Dhan and Sudhir never had had milk to drink. There were hundreds of cows in Calcutta but they were not kept for their milk. They were a sacred animal allowed to go where they pleased and do as they pleased, for a cow could do no wrong. Crows screamed to each other from the trees and fearless little birds hopped closed to the pass-ers-by, hoping to be fed. Sometimes the air was clouded with birds, little and big, flying from one place to another. There were vultures who helped to keep the country clean by eating up dead flesh and garbage and all foul-smelling things.

Dhan's sahib was away now in the mountains, so that was one reason why he had time to go to the station. Dhan was a sweeper in the sahib's big house, but even if he had been sweeping there today he would still have gone to the station to see Gandhi. There was always time to do what you really wanted to do in India. The poor people didn't have money like the sahibs but they had more time.

They were passing the sahib's house now. Dhan looked up to the window of the office and saw Jagdish, the pet crow, sitting on the window sill preening his feathers. Most of the crows weren't named, there were so many. They flew in and out of the office all day and lit on the sahib's desk and sometimes were a nuisance, and Dhan would have to wave his broom at them, but he never shooed Jagdish away. He was a wise bird and you didn't dare interfere with him or he might peck you the next time. Even the sahib liked him and fed him. Dhan spent hours when the sahib was out, playing with the bird. Crows never came to the small huts where Dhan lived. They liked to fly high and only chose to come in second-story windows.

The brothers paused for a moment in front of a merchant who squatted on the sidewalk. He held a large, round, woven tray brimming with colored candies, green, yellow and pink. Flies crawled over the sweets but the boys were thinking only of how they would taste and looked at them with hungry eyes. The man glanced around to see that there were no other boys ready to descend on him, then smiled and motioned them to take a piece. They reached out timidly and dropped the candy into their mouths. The man smiled at them again as they thanked him, and spat out some betel juice which made a large spot of red that looked like blood. All of the merchants chewed betel nut.

As they came nearer to Howrah Station the crowds thickened. Thousands of people were coming to see Gandhi arrive. Dhan and Sudhir nudged through the crowds. When they reached the station they pushed their way up to the water hut marked "For Hindus." A few yards away from it was a similar hut marked "For Muslims."

The man in charge of the hut objected to giving them water. He said it must be saved for the train arrivals. A few people held up small vessels for him to fill from his large brass jar. First he poured some water over their hands so that they could be clean before drinking, then they rinsed out their mouths with a little water and drank. Dhan and Sudhir held out their hands and the man grudgingly poured a few drops over them. Then not having any vessels to drink from, they made cups of their hands and drank after rinsing out their mouths.

It would be an hour before the train was due, but since

trains were seldom on time in India there would probably
be hours to wait. The two brothers sat down on the station
platform where they thought the third-class carriage in
which Gandhi always rode would pull in. There was a
great deal of bustle on the platform. Some of the people
were naked except for loin cloths; there were women carrying jars, there were variations of colors in the women's
saris and shawls. The men wore white dhotis, a long cloth
wound about their bodies. A few of them wore a Gandhi
cap like an over-seas cap only white. These were worn by
members of the India National Congress, a political party.
People spoke to each other in various languages.

"I hear the train!" Sudhir shouted to Dhan. He leaped
to his feet, and the boys pushed to the edge of the platform. They could see the train a long way off, running
slowly along the shining track. There were people sitting
on the roof and clinging to the sides of the cars. There was
never enough room inside for all the people who wanted to
ride on trains in India. It was all right in the dry season
such as now, but when the rains came it would be a different matter.

The train slowed down. Dhan, pulling Sudhir, ducked
under and through the crowd until they stood right where
Gandhi stepped out on the platform. Dhan was breathless
with excitement, but he hadn't pictured the man that he
saw. Why, he's like a monkey, he thought. This was not
saying anything horrid about Gandhi, for Dhan admired
monkeys almost more than people. Gandhi was a wise
monkey; his bright, penetrating eyes saw and knew everything. Dhan noticed his large ears, and as he stared,
Gandhi turned and met his eyes. Dhan made a little salute
and Gandhi smiled almost as if he would like to laugh
with Dhan but he was being swept on by the people who
were crowding close. Governor Casey's car waited for him.

Gandhi wrapped his white dhoti about him and stepped into the car. His thin legs looked frail, almost too thin to hold him up, Dhan thought.

The car went slowly across the bridge over the Hooghly River, with the people following.

"What's he going to do? Why did he come?" Sudhir asked, as they hurried along.

"Don't you know how Manilal has been out every night raiding the Muslims? Gandhiji says that we mustn't fight. He's coming to bring peace. The Muslims don't want us. We don't want them. Now that the English are going to give us independence, the Muslims want Pakistan for themselves. All of them ought to leave, then, and go to their own country. I think Manilal is a hero to fight the Muslims."

Dhan spoke of their brother, Manilal. It was he who had explained to Dhan what they were fighting about. Manilal was their mother's favorite. He was sixteen, almost a man. Another child had been born between him and Dhan, who was twelve, but had died when he was a baby. In India death was sorrowful but an ever present occurrence. Sometimes more children died than lived in a family.

Manilal was one of the leaders of the gangs who went out at night to raid the Muslim shops in Calcutta. The Hindus and Muslims had different religions, and how they worshipped was more important than life itself.

The hot sun beat down on the people as they followed Gandhi's car to the Government House. Gandhi had disappeared behind closed doors when the boys arrived there. The crowds swirled and flowed into the courtyard like a swollen river. Dhan had never been so near to the beautiful building before. He had always looked at its imposing structure through the high iron fence surrounding the grounds and courtyard.

The people waited patiently in the heat, knowing that their hero after conferring with the Governor would come out and speak to them. At last the door opened and the small, frail man in his dhoti and sandals and spectacles stood there before them and raised his hand to silence them as they shouted greeting. Dhan waited for the sound of his voice. How could it be heard above such a noise? But suddenly the people became quiet. It was as still as an Indian landscape after a storm.

"India is great," Gandhi said in his small but powerful voice, "only because she has always followed the way of peace."

Dhan listened for more, but the slim figure turned about and withdrew into the house again. He was disappointed, but the people seemed satisfied as they murmured to each other and gradually withdrew from the courtyard and thinned and scattered on the streets again.

As the boys neared home they stopped at a fire hydrant to bathe, for they were hot. Some boys had turned on the water and were washing under it and laughing. There was an indentation in the pavement which filled up with a few inches of water. The boys took turns sitting in it and splashing themselves, like English sparrows taking a bath in a puddle.

That night as usual Dhan's mother served them their evening meal. She dished out hot rice from the kettle over the fire and dal from another kettle. Dal was a thick, brown gravy which was poured over the rice. There were also some bits of fish tonight. The family, who had thoroughly washed their hands, ate with their fingers and after eating rinsed them in a bowl of water which their mother brought to each in turn, beginning with their father.

Manilal had been silent through the meal. There usually was little said, but Manilal frowned tonight. Dhan knew he was planning and waiting. Soon a figure darkened the doorway and Manilal rose with excuses and said he would go out with his friend. The friend bowed to the family, and then without more words they left.

Dhan managed to slip after them, unnoticed. It was dark now. As he followed them along the dirt path, he looked through the opened doors of the huts and saw the oil lights flickering on the faces of families as they sat at the evening meal. But Dhan was not thinking of those sad, dark faces. His heart thumped rapidly. Something exciting was going to happen tonight. He knew it from Manilal's brooding expression and his shining black eyes as he greeted his friend.

He followed them out into the blazing lights of the main city where the crowds thronged. Why were they here? Where were all these people going? Were they waiting for something, Dhan wondered. But he must keep up with Manilal, which wasn't so easy now. The two figures ahead of him dodged through the crowd. Dhan saw them pause in front of a shop. He remembered the shop. He had often looked in its windows at the bright jewelry there and imagined the pearls and diamonds running through his fingers.

Suddenly a shot was fired. It must have been the friend's pistol, for Manilal threw a huge stone at the same time. Glass crashed on to the sidewalk. Now there was shooting everywhere and people turning on each other, and the owner of the shop screaming, "Allah, Allah have mercy on me—I am ruined!" Dhan could see his features twisting in rage and sorrow and his fez falling over his face. There were more shots but Dhan didn't know who was shooting. It might be Manilal or his friend or anybody, there was so much confusion.

Now the people were pushing into the shop and looting the place. Dhan was carried along by the crowd. His eyes were wide in astonishment. He saw a man dangling a string of pearls in his hand and then he heard a shot from a policeman and the man fell to the floor close to where Dhan stood. He must get away quickly. They would think he had part in it. But he hesitated a moment not being able to take his eyes from the body of the fallen man who still grasped the pearls in his hand. He was dying, Dhan knew. The man moaned and Dhan noticed the blood oozing on to his dhoti. He shuddered in revulsion.

Dhan turned about, wedged his way out of the crowd and ran. Not until he came to the dirt path leading to his home did he stop. He drew in his breath and sighed with relief. Here was quietness and safety. A few men strolled. Most of the lights had gone from the huts. An occasional red glow brightened the darkness here and there where the evening fire still burned. In the distance Dhan heard someone blowing on a conch shell. It wasn't music, for the notes rose and fell without relation to each other; a few high and then dropping to another level, like mournful words repeated over and over.

Moonlight silvered the thatched roofs of the huts. Usually Dhan took the moon for granted. It was only a pretty round plate as it came up over the horizon. But now it touched him with its cool serenity, its harmonizing light. He had witnessed a horrible death tonight. He felt a wordless warmth move through him as he thought of the families lying on their mats in the huts in the close hot air. Here they seemed safe from sudden death, but it might come to them at any hour when hatred charged the air as it had tonight. Why should they die without reason? All in an instant he remembered the words Gandhi had spoken that morning. "India is great because she has followed the

way of peace," he had said. Dhan felt quiet now and reassured as he stepped inside their hut. Even the thought
of Manilal coming in later bringing with him the taint of
evil could not disturb the new love he found in his heart.

The riots continued and a few days later Dhan rushed
to his mother. "Gandhiji has come to live in our street,"
he cried. "He and Suhrawardy Sahib are going to show us
that Hindus and Muslims can live together. He's only a
few doors from us, Mother. I looked in and saw him sitting
on a mat talking to Suhrawardy Sahib and some other people. The Mahatma says it's the only way to convince us
that people can live in peace if they try. Father says Suhrawardy Sahib is a Muslim; he says he's a bad man even
though he was Premier of Bengal once."

"Gandhiji is a saint," his mother said softly. She was
nursing the baby at her breast, and as she looked at Dhan
her eyes were tender and mournful. "I'll be able to see him
now. I'll stand outside and look at him for the first time."

"You'll have a hard time seeing him, Mother. Everybody
is there. They had to ask the people to get out of the house.
There was no air left for the Mahatma."

The mother laid the baby down on the mat. Loud voices
rang outside on the street, and they heard a movement of
people.

Dhan ran to the door. "Something has happened," he
shouted.

"Wait, I'll come," his mother said.

They ran along the dirt path with the hurrying people.
There were cries of hatred and despair as they came to the
house where Gandhi was. Dhan looked and saw his
brother, Manilal, throw a stone at the house. Other stones
flew through the air. Some of the men were shouting imprecations against Gandhi. The noise grew louder and

then suddenly stopped. Gandhi and Mr. Suhrawardy stood in the doorway. A flying stone grazed Gandhi's thin body but he seemed not to notice it. Dhan could see the mark on his wrinkled flesh for he wore no dhoti today, only a loin cloth and sandals on his feet. He looked frail and old except for his penetrating eyes.

Dhan watched his brother fold his arms and scowl and look down as if he were ashamed. He had thought of Manilal as a hero once, but now he felt only anger toward him. Tears were running down his mother's face. Surely Gandhiji would raise his hand or Suhrawardy Sahib protest, but they stood utterly still. The mob began to murmur. They must be feeling foolish for how could they attack when there was no resistance. The thing that they would fight wasn't there. Dhan smiled to himself. He was glad the men were in disgrace, for he realized that Gandhi was the conqueror as he stood with a calm, bright expression on his face. Gradually the men disappeared, grumbling and defeated.

As the days passed a new quietness came to the street and to the city. Muslims and Hindus were speaking to each other. The people smiled in greeting, and Rashid, Dhan's hated Muslim, gave him first place at the pump. Religious processions formed and marched through the city of Calcutta. Dhan and his mother went out into the open space where Gandhi addressed the multitudes and people of all religions gathered to hear him. Sometimes he would pray a Muslim prayer and all would bow their heads, sometimes a Hindu prayer. Dhan felt the pulsation of the people run through him, not knowing in words why he was so moved, why he came to listen with his mother to the emaciated man with spectacles and small insistent voice that could be heard above every disturbance.

"It is a miracle," his mother said as she and Dhan

strolled home in the warm Indian dusk. "A sweet wind has come to our city—peace has come."

But sitting at the evening meal Dhan felt that peace had not come to their home. Manilal brooded. His expression had changed, though, from alert anger to thoughts about something that Dhan could not guess.

Then like a dark cloud appearing on a sunny day, a shadow crept again over the city. There were stories of refugees in the Punjab, both Hindu and Muslim, suffering torture. Riots started again where for a few days there had been peace.

Dhan, standing outside of Gandhi's hut, heard the people say that the Mahatma had decided to fast until peace should be restored. He ran home to tell his mother. His heart was heavy.

"He'll die," Dhan said to his mother. "He's so thin. How can he live when he doesn't eat?" He felt tears burn in his eyes. There was love in his heart now for the little man. It would be a terrible thing for him to die, a terrible loss for the people who loved him. His mother clasped her hands and breathed a prayer.

While Gandhi fasted there were peace processions through the streets. Dhan joined in these. He was swept along from one excitement to another and all the time he kept thinking of the frail saint wasting away while he fasted perhaps until he died. Groups of people entered into prayer for peace that they might save the life of their Mahatma, and that they might save India from bloodshed.

One day Manilal came home at noon. Dhan looked at him questioningly. He usually was away all day, but now he had come home. Dhan had been frightened when he saw him strolling down the path. He'd probably got into trouble with the police. But as he came into their hut,

Manilal smiled at Dhan and went in and spoke to their mother.

Soon about fifty men gathered outside of their hut and Manilal went out and joined them. Dhan followed. The men had guns and knives but their faces were strangely quiet. If they were going to kill the Mahatma, surely they would be muttering foul words and gesticulating in anger. But they formed in a group and walked quietly down the path in the bright, hot sun. They stopped outside of the Mahatma's house, and Manilal went ahead of them through the door. Dhan watched the men follow him in, as many as could find room. Dhan slipped in unnoticed. Gandhi was speaking to Manilal. Mr. Suhrawardy was there too, not speaking but smiling.

"We have come to bring you these," Manilal said, addressing Gandhi. He held up a rifle and a knife and the other men held up their guns and knives. The Mahatma sat quietly, looking at them thoughtfully out of his small, quick eyes. There was a flush on his face. He looked too thin to breathe, almost, Dhan thought. And then he smiled and spoke to Manilal as he sat with his legs crossed on the mat.

"We pledge ourselves," Manilal said in a new, solemn voice that Dhan had never heard before, "not to participate in any more violence—we pledge ourselves to die if need be to prevent violence."

There was silence in the room as each man took his gun and knife and laid it at the feet of the Mahatma. There was only the sound of the click, click of the rifles as they laid them down. Then the Mahatma spoke.

"Your only weapon now is love," he said, "but it is infinitely greater than the sword."

*   *   *

On that afternoon Gandhi broke his seventy-three-hour fast. Calcutta remained quiet. Three days later, Gandhi, frail and fast-marked, left Calcutta for Delhi and the Punjab. Thousands of Hindus and Muslims and others gathered to bid him goodbye. Many of them had taken the vow unto death to maintain the communal harmony which he had brought. In temples, mosques and churches prayers were said and on the previous day thousands had participated in a day-long fast.

Dhan and Sudher and their mother and Manilal stood together and waved goodbye to the man whom they would never see again.

Retold, by Edith Warner Johnson, from an incident reported by Dr. William Stuart Nelson.

AN ILL WIND

"METHINKS this west wind bodes us no good," said William Rotch in an undertone to his wife, as he turned from the open window one morning in the summer of 1778.

"Why, Father, what harm can come from the west wind?" inquired twelve-year-old Thomas, who was always hearing things he was not expected to hear. "I thought the west wind was our friend, and brought the whaling ships safe to port."

"Yea, son, so it was in the old days, but, alas, we peaceful Nantucket folk can no longer ply our trade. Thou knowest, not a whaling ship has gone out for many a day. My fear is that today's wind may give a British privateer a chance to enter our Sherburne harbor."

"What? Not a full-rigged ship with guns and armed men? Why should they come to Nantucket? They know well that we are no fighting folk."

"True, my boy. Yet we be known as a thrifty community, and might be worth a visit. These privateers plunder where they can."

"Joe Macy told me that vessels flying the British flag have been sighted off the coast a dozen times during the past month."

"That is so, but they could not enter our harbor on the east wind that fortunately for us has been blowing all this long while. I shall go down into the town to see what tidings there be. Nay, stay thou with thy mother and sisters while I am gone. This may be a serious matter."

Without further words, William Rotch put on his broad-brimmed Quaker hat and strode down the street.

Ahead of him groups of anxious and excited townspeople

were rapidly moving toward the wharf. Many of the old
sea captains had their spy glasses with them the better to
observe the formidable ship coming before the wind into
the harbor, all her white sails set, and a wicked array of
guns, visible even to those watchers who had no spy glasses.
At the masthead floated the Union Jack, and the decks
seemed to be crowded with gunners and sailors.

Old Asa Prindle offered his glass to William Rotch without comment. William looked through it at the tall ship as
she came about, spilled the wind from her flapping sails,
and prepared to anchor where her guns could best command the defenseless town. He could easily see a fine-
looking officer directing the maneuvers, and borne by the
stiff wind across the water, the boatswain's voice could be
heard giving orders to lower away a boat from the ship's
side.

Into this boat presently descended the crew, and then
the fine-looking officer already noticed by William Rotch.
After him followed six men with side-arms. Rowed by
powerful strokes of the oars, the boat rapidly approached
the wharf.

"No doubt of it now. They come for plunder," said old
Asa.

"Suppose I talk with the commander on behalf of the
town?" suggested William. "If I can get him to come to
my house it may be well, for with the privations our people
have undergone on account of the war someone might
speak from his heart and anger our visitors into even worse
measures than they contemplate."

"Our fate is safer in thy hands, William, than in our
own. Do as seems best to thee, good neighbor."

"So say we all," came in many voices from the crowd
surrounding William and old Asa.

The ship's boat made for the lee side of the wharf. With

a boat-hook she was held to the tall piles while the painter was made fast. Out jumped the officer and his bodyguard of six armed men. William Rotch advanced to meet him with the friendly greeting that a loved and long-expected visitor might receive.

"This is William Rotch who bids thee welcome to Nantucket, friend. What may thy name be?"

"Sir Conway-Etherege, in the King's service," replied the officer, stiffly.

"I invite thee to come to my house—and thy friends likewise," said William, regarding calmly the six men with two pistols apiece in their belts.

"My men will await my orders, here," replied the officer.

Sir Conway-Etherege evidently thought his way was smoothed before him by this encounter with a friendly Loyalist inhabitant. He moved off beside William along the pleasant street up to a row of substantial-looking houses. William led his guest to the middle one of three large dwellings and bade him enter. It was nearly noon.

"I would like thee to take dinner with me."

"Thank you, with pleasure."

William then presented his guest to his wife and introduced his children, before they sat down together to a homely, ample meal. The younger Rotch children's eyes were shining with suppressed excitement, but they heeded their mother's hasty instructions to ask no questions, given when, to her astonishment, she saw her husband bringing in this unknown and possibly dangerous guest to share their dinner.

William treated the commander kindly and seemed to enjoy his conversation. The islanders had, as the officer knew, been cut off from contact with the outside world by the war. The officer furnished the news of the day, the current jests, and even the idle gossip of the mainland as it had come to him through English channels. From time to time he regarded William quizzically, as if he did not quite know how to approach his errand, although it was foremost in both their minds.

Finally they rose from the table. With the manners of his station in society, Sir Conway-Etherege made Elizabeth Rotch a flowery speech of appreciation, bowed over her hand and kissed it respectfully, at which Thomas had some ado to keep from snickering. The children followed their mother from the room.

"I take it, Mr. Rotch, from your signal courtesies to me, that you are on the King's side. Can you tell me how and where I had best begin the day's work? As you must know, I command yonder privateer, which has gone up and down the coast bent on plunder. Very successfully, too. We take pains to see that our guns rake all the important structures and districts of a town before we enter upon negotiations. As you see, your little hamlet is completely at our mercy. I anticipate no unpleasant resistance."

"There will be none," said William.

"Then how and where do you advise me to begin? The afternoon is advancing."

William smiled.

"I don't know of a better place to begin than here in my house. I am better able to bear the loss than anyone else. We have a store of silver plate, good, serviceable blankets, also linens; and in the cellar, supplies of food of various kinds. Thou art mistaken in supposing me to be on the side of those engaged in warfare."

Sir Conway-Etherege was greatly taken aback. He gazed at William with unconcealed curiosity. Never had he run across a man of his sort.

"Are there any more men like you on Nantucket?"

"There are many better men," answered William.

"Do you say so, indeed! I'd have to see them before I could believe it."

"Then come with me. I shall be glad to introduce some of our islanders to thee."

The officer followed William down the steps and out into the street again. This was a new experience to the commander of the privateer, and he did not know what to make of it.

Presently they entered a store where merchandise was sold. The store did not have a prosperous air, for the townspeople had little money for trade these days. Yet it had once done a large business, and was spacious and well stocked.

William led the officer to the proprietor and introduced them.

"Our visitor wants to know what sort of people we are. I tell him that last winter thou wert the distributor of four hundred barrels of flour among the poor on the island. And yet I doubt if I, or any man, know the full extent of what thou hast done to help the needy."

Amazed at this generosity on the part of a man with his living to make, the officer entered into conversation with the proprietor who told him of gifts of money which had found their way from William Rotch's pockets to households in distress, without anyone's suspecting him of being the donor. William hurried the officer out of the door at this. Further down toward the wharf they entered a store that sold dry goods.

"Good day, Peter," said William. "This officer from yonder ship in the harbor wishes to meet the man who gave away blankets, dress goods, and stout shoes last winter when the poor were in dire want."

"He might better turn around and meet thee, William. None of us has done what thou hast done. We but follow thy lead."

The face of William was rosier than even the brisk west wind had made it, as he led the officer out again into the street.

"My friends are modest," he said. "I can better afford to help others than they can. Dost thou care to cross the street and meet more of our people?"

"Thank you, no. I find it hard to believe that there are three such men as you in the world. A whole street full of them would be almost too many. Thank you for your courtesy and forebearance. Farewell, my friend. I shall not forget Nantucket."

With that the officer grasped William's hand and shook it heartily. He looked once again up the leafy, beautiful street, and out toward the white-capped harbor where his ship with its deadly guns lay threateningly at anchor.

Groups of men were still watching and talking on the wharf. The sailors and the armed bodyguard were puzzled to know what had delayed their commander so long. Here he was coming at last. Well, the excitement of looting and plundering was worth waiting for. As Sir Conway-Etherege came briskly toward them, they saluted. His orders were quick and short. The sailors took their places at the oars, and rowed the officer back to his ship. The ship weighed anchor, trimmed her sails, and to the surprised relief of all Nantucket, sailed peaceably out of sight

Lam 3·30   Luke 6·29.

WHERE LOVE IS,
THERE GOD IS ALSO

IN THE city lived Martin, a shoemaker. He lived in a basement, in a little room with one window. The window looked out on the street. Through the window he used to watch the people passing by: although only the feet could be seen, yet by the boots Martin knew their owners. He had lived long in one place, and few pairs of boots in his district had not been in his hands at some time or other. He was never out of work because all knew that he did his work well and kept his promises.

He lived all alone in his basement. His wife had died and also his children, so he was glad to watch the people passing on the street, just for company. At night, when his work was done, he would take a New Testament in large print from a high shelf and read until all the kerosene in his lamp had burned out.

Once it happened that Martin read until late into the night. He was reading the Gospel of Luke; and he came to the verses, "And unto him that smiteth thee on the one cheek offer also the other; and him that taketh away thy cloak forbid not to take thy coat also. Give to every man that asketh of thee; and of him that taketh away thy goods ask them not again. And as ye would that men should do to you, do ye also to them likewise." And then he read about the Pharisee who asked Jesus to supper and then was not kind to him.

Martin took off his spectacles, put them down upon the book, and thought to himself.

"That Pharisee must have been such a man as I am.

I, too, have thought only of myself—how I might have my tea, be warm and comfortable, but never to think about my guest. He thought about himself, but there was not the least care taken of the guest. And who was his guest? The Lord himself. If he had come to me, should I have done the same way?"

Martin rested his head upon both his arms, and did not notice how he fell fast asleep.

"Martin!" suddenly seemed to sound in his ears.

Martin started in his sleep: "Who is here?"

Again he fell into a doze. Suddenly he plainly heard—

"Martin! Ah, Martin! look tomorrow on the street. I am coming."

Martin awoke, rose from the chair, began to rub his eyes. He did not know whether he had heard the words in a dream or in reality. He turned down the light and went to bed.

At daybreak next morning, Martin rose, said his prayer to God, lighted the stove, put on the soup to cook and water to heat, tied on his shoemaker's apron, and sat down by the window to work.

As he worked, he thought about his dream of the night before; and now, when any one passed, he bent down so that he could see not only the feet but also the face. Presently there came alongside of the window an old street-cleaner with a shovel in his hands. Martin knew him by his felt boots. The old man's name was Stephen; and a neighboring merchant, out of charity, gave him a home with him. Stephen began to shovel away the snow from in front of Martin's window. Then he stopped and leaned his shovel against the wall. He was an old, broken-down man; evidently he had not strength enough even to shovel snow. Martin said to himself, "I will give him some tea. The water must be boiling by this time." He laid down his awl, put the hot water on the table, made the tea, and tapped with his finger on the glass. Stephen turned around and came to the window. Martin beckoned to him, and went to open the door.

"Come in, warm yourself a little," he said. "You must be cold."

"May Christ reward you for this! my bones ache," said Stephen. He came in, shook off the snow, tried to wipe his feet so as not to soil the floor, but staggered.

"Don't trouble to wipe your feet. I will clean up the snow myself; we are used to such things. Come in and sit down," said Martin. "Drink a cup of tea."

The two men had their tea together, but Stephen noticed that Martin kept looking out on the street.

"Are you expecting any one?" he asked.

Then Martin told him how he had been reading about the Pharisee who did not receive Christ with honor, and how he had had a dream in which he had heard Christ say that he was coming to see him that day, and how it had got into his head so that he could not think of anything else. Then he saw that Stephen's cup was empty and asked him to have some more tea. But Stephen rose and shook his head.

"Thank you, Martin," he said, "for treating me so kindly."

"You are welcome; come in again; always glad to see a friend," said Martin.

A little later, Martin saw a woman pass his window with a child in her arms. She stopped and stood by the wall with her back to the wind, and he saw that she was dressed in shabby summer clothes and had nothing to wrap the child in. From behind the glass he could hear the child crying. He hurried to the door and cried: "Here, my good woman!" The woman heard him and turned around.

"Why are you standing in the cold with the child? Come into my room where it is warm: you can manage it better. Right in this way!"

The woman was astonished, but she followed Martin, who led her into the room and to a chair.

"There," he said, "sit down, my good woman, nearer to the stove where you can get warm."

Then he went to the stove, poured some hot soup into a dish and put it on the table.

"Sit down and eat," he said to the woman, "and I will mind the little one. You see, I once had children of my own; I know how to handle them."

The woman sat down at the table and ate the soup while Martin minded the baby. In the meantime, she told him her story. Her husband had gone to hunt work and she had not heard from him for seven months. She had been a cook but was now three months without a place. Now she had nothing to eat and had pawned her last shawl so that she had no warm clothes.

Martin went to the wall where his own clothes hung and succeeded in finding an old coat. He gave it to the woman.

"It is a poor thing," he said, "yet you may put it to some use."

The woman burst into tears as she took the coat.

"May God bless you!" she cried. "He must have sent me himself to your window. My little child would have frozen to death."

Martin smiled. "Indeed he must have sent you," he said; and then he remembered his dream of the night before—he had forgotten it in his care for the woman. He told her of it—how he had heard the voice, how Christ had promised to come to see him that day.

"All things are possible," said the woman. She rose, put

on the coat, wrapped up her little child in it; and as she
started to go, she thanked Martin again.

"Take this, for Christ's sake," said Martin, giving her a
piece of money. "Get back your shawl." Then he went
with her to the door.

The window grew darker, but Martin still watched as
he worked. For some time there was nothing out of the
ordinary. Then an old apple-woman stopped right in front
of his window. Only a few apples were left in her basket,
and over her shoulder she carried a bag full of chips. She
must have gathered them up in some new building and was
on her way home. The bag was so heavy that she wanted
to shift it to the other shoulder. So she lowered the bag
upon the sidewalk, stood the basket with the apples on a
little post, and began to shake down the splinters in the
bag. And while she was shaking her bag, a little boy with
a torn cap came along, picked up an apple from the basket,
and was about to run away; but the old woman noticed it
and caught him by the sleeve. The boy began to struggle,
but the old woman grasped him with both hands, knocked
off his cap, and caught him by the hair.

Martin rushed out to the street. "I did not take it!" he
heard the boy say. "Let me go!"

"Let him go," said Martin, taking the boy by the arm.
"Forgive him, for Christ's sake."

The old woman let him loose. The boy tried to run, but
Martin held him back.

"Ask the little grandmother's forgiveness," he said, "and
don't you ever do it again: I saw you take the apple."

With tears in his eyes, the boy began to ask forgiveness.

"That's right; and now, here's an apple for you." Martin
got an apple from the basket, and gave it to the boy. "I
will pay you for both, little grandmother," he said to the
woman.

The old woman could not understand at first. She thought the boy ought to be punished so that he would remember it for a whole week. But Martin told her that he ought to be forgiven, as he had only been thoughtless and was sorry.

"Of course, it is a childish trick. God be with him," said she, pointing to the boy.

She was just about to lift the bag to her shoulder, when the boy ran up, and said, "Let me carry it, little grandmother: it is on my way."

The old woman nodded her head and put the bag on the boy's back.

Side by side they both passed along the street. And the old woman had not even allowed Martin to pay for the apples.

Martin stood gazing after them until they disappeared. Then he returned to his room, and as it was dark, he put away his work, lighted the lamp, and took the Gospels down from the shelf. He intended to open the book at the very place where he had yesterday put a piece of leather as a mark, but it happened to open at another place; and the moment he opened the Testament, he remembered last night's dream. And as soon as he remembered it, it seemed as though he heard some one stepping about behind him. He looked around and there, in the dark corner, it seemed as though people were standing: he was at a loss to know who they were. And a voice whispered in his ear,

"Martin, ah, Martin! did you not recognize me?"

"Who?" uttered Martin.

Then he seemed to see Stephen, and the woman and the child, and the old apple-woman with the boy. One by one, they stepped out of the dark corner, smiled at him, and vanished.

Martin was glad as he thought of them. He put on his spectacles, and began to read the Bible where it had happened to open. On the upper part of the page he read,

"For I was an hungered, and ye gave me meat: I was thirsty and ye gave me to drink: I was a stranger and ye took me in . . ."

And on the lower part of the page he read this;

"Inasmuch as ye have done it unto one of the least of these my brethren, ye have done it unto me."

And Martin understood that his dream did not deceive him; that Christ had really visited him that day, and that he really had received him.

Adapted by Frances M. Dadmun from Nathan Haskell Dole's translation of the story by Leo Tolstoy in "Living Together." Copyright by The Beacon Press. Used with permission.

THE WORD OF A GENTLEMAN

DARKNESS had fallen on the camp of David Livingstone beside the Zambesi River. The African forest was lonely and terrifying, for the explorers had followed the river beyond the territory of the friendly natives into a country made suspicious by the depredations of the Portuguese slave traders.

"But, see for yourselves," Livingstone had said to the ominous group of natives who had watched them making camp, "I am not like the Bazimka," and he pointed to his straight hair and the fair skin on his arms and chest.

The savages, however, had remained suspicious. It was apparent that these strangers were of a different race from the swarthy Portuguese, but all strangers were suspect. So muttering and hostile, they had withdrawn to take counsel.

Livingstone retired to his tent to decide what should be the next move. Upon his decision rested the fate of the expedition; not only the lives of his faithful followers but the results of months of painful effort to open up this "dark continent". In order to proceed with their journey it would be necessary to cross the Loangwa River which flowed into the Zambesi at this point. Should they attempt to get away under cover of darkness? Should they go forward or back? One thing Livingstone knew without a shadow of doubt—that he was called upon to do a particular service—to open up Africa to civilization—but how?

The hours passed and still he pondered. Finally he lighted a candle and taking up his Testament opened it and read, "All power is given unto me in heaven and in earth. Go ye therefore and teach all nations—and lo, I am with you always, even unto the end of the world."

"It is the word of a gentleman of the most sacred and strictest honor, and there's an end on't," he said. "I shall not cross furtively at night. Should a man such as I flee? Nay, verily, I shall go even now and take observations for latitude and longitude."

Next morning with the early summer sunrise the explorers were up and prepared to make the crossing. The natives from all of the surrounding country were up also. Armed and threatening they collected around Livingstone and his men to watch for the next move. The native women and children had been sent away—a sure sign that violence was intended.

Livingstone calmly went on with his preparations. The savages watched his every move. The Loangwa is a mighty river, a mile broad, and the travellers would be utterly defenseless while making the crossing. The natives could afford to hold back until the explorers actually shoved off. Besides it would take several loads to ferry across all the goods, equipment, cattle, and men.

"But, look, what is the White Chief doing? He is displaying a little round, gold box. It is full of wheels and makes a clucking sound. So that is the reason the white men wear all those unnecessary clothes—to carry that funny little box. And all to tell time with! Poh, doesn't the White Chief know how to tell time by the sun? See, what is he doing now? He has a shiny stone that you can see through. And he has lighted a fire with it! He says he has pulled down the heat from the sun. He knows something about the sun after all. Maybe he could teach us the secret."

The mob closed in, all attention and interest.

Livingstone showed his pen and his pencil. He unpacked all of his personal kit—scientific instruments, clothing, everything that would hold their attention, demonstrating their use and allowing the savages to handle anything they wished.

Meanwhile, trip by trip, the expedition had been getting safely across the river.

At length all were over except those who were to go in the canoe with Livingstone. The great explorer offered a friendly hand, "Thank you, O Chief, for your kindness," he said. "I wish you peace. Farewell." And with a wave to the crowd he climbed into the canoe and shoved off.

SUSAN AND THE WITCH

SUSAN's way back to the village lay by the Old Witch's Cottage. She hated passing it and always went very fast and tried to look the other way. For Susan knew that Mollie was a wicked old woman, who had sold her soul to the Devil. She looked such a scarecrow with her ragged clothes and wild matted hair and long nails like claws. Susan knew that she had the evil eye, and could turn it on to anyone she had a grudge against, so that his corn became mildewed, or his horse fell lame, or his cow ceased to give milk, or one of his family had an accident.

How often had the villagers vowed they would burn down her cottage, Mollie and all! Or they would drag her before the magistrates and have her tried as a witch and condemned to be burned at the stake. For everybody believed in witches in those days, and, if you had lived three-hundred years ago, as Susan did, you would have believed in them too. So far, however, the villagers had left Old Mollie unhurt, though the children threw stones at her and her cat, and ran after her calling:

> Cock and hen; cock and hen,
> Frighten the devil out of his den!

Susan herself had done it many times when she was a little girl.

Now Susan's eyes turned involuntarily to Mollie's home. It was a broken-down hovel. How the rain must pour in, thought Susan, and how did she keep her chickens safe from foxes with that poor little fence? There was her broom against the wall. Did she really fly on its stick to the Devil's feasts?

33

Then she saw Old Mollie. She was sitting at her back door, one hand clasping her head and the other idly stroking her cat. At that moment she looked just a tired lonely old woman. Susan couldn't help feeling sorry for her. It must be terrible to be hated by everybody. Even her father had once told her that Mollie had lost her soul, and he was always right.

Just then Old Mollie saw her. She ran to the fence shouting and waving her arms. Susan wanted to run away but curiosity held her.

"Tha can tell Farmer Brown," she shouted, shaking her fist, "Ah'll be even wi' that boy of his'n. Stole yan o' my chicks, he did. Ah see'd 'im. Owd Mollie sees everything, she does. And Owd Mollie'll be fixing her eye on that thief of a boy when he don't know. Tha can tell him."

Susan shrank before the old woman's threatening finger, and hurried on.

"How does she live?" she wondered. "She looks just a bag o' bones. She sells her simples sometimes, but that can't keep her."

Just then she spied Bob Brown over the hedge.

"Here, Bob, did thee steal Owd Mollie's chicks?"

"That I did," said Bob gleefully. "She never see'd me." Then suddenly. "How didst thee know, Sue?"

"Owd Mollie did see thee. She's told me to tell thy father she'll be even wi' thee. Thee knows what that means?"

"Thee won't tell Father, Sue?" asked Bob anxiously, "He'll thrash me. He's afeared o' Owd Mollie."

"And tha had best be afeared too. Th'art a silly loon to be setting her eye on thee like this. Mebbe I won't tell thy dad, but 'tis for Owd Mollie's sake, not thine."

"For Owd Mollie's sake! What dos't mean, Sue? She's naught but a vile hag."

"No," said Susan, "but do thee keep thy hands off her chicks." She hurried on home.

Susan Abbott lived with her parents in a village six miles from Lancaster under Pendle Hill. Their cottage was a comfortable one. Her father, Roger Abbott, was the village blacksmith, a man who, until a short time before, had been universally loved and respected by his neighbors. Everybody used to bring their troubles to Roger at the smithy behind the cottage, just as they brought their horses to be shod.

But things were different now. He had given offense to many of his old friends, and particularly the Vicar, by leaving his old Parish Church, where he had been warden, to join the sect of the Quakers and attend meetings of George Fox's followers out on Pendle Hill.

At that time the Quakers were spreading like wildfire over England, and Susan's father was only one of many thousands who dropped their tools or left their plows to learn and preach their newly found doctrines.

For longer and longer periods did Roger Abbott feel called upon to travel afield spreading his good news. Susan's mother often went with him, Tom being left in charge of the forge, and Susan, with the help of an elderly cousin, in charge of the house. Susan was only twelve but a girl of that age was regarded, in those days, as almost grown-up. Her brother, Tom, was now twenty, hardworking and clever. He could shoe horses and make and mend farm-implements almost as well as his father. But he could not give wise advice, and the villagers missed Roger.

Roger called his fellow-thinkers, "Friends," but he accepted with a smile the queer name of "Quakers," given to them by their scoffers. He refused to quarrel with his old companions and remained kind and helpful as ever. But Susan, who, like Tom, had been left to decide for herself whether she would become a Quaker or not and was thinking much about it, felt sadly that her home was a less pleasant place than before. Fewer friendly neighbors dropped in.

On the afternoon that Susan came back from her encounter with Old Mollie, she found to her joy that her father had come home. After supper, as they were sitting round the lamp, Susan suddenly dropped the sock she was knitting and said: "Father, do not the Quakers believe there be good in everybody?"

"Yea, child, in each of us there shines the Light that was in Christ, in each of us there is a Seed planted by God."

"But what about Mollie?" persisted Susan. "Everyone says—parson says it too—that she hath sold her soul to the Devil. Is she not bad right through?"

"Nay, Susan," said her father after a pause. "The Light of God is in every man. It is there in Old Mollie, though mebbe but a glimmer and hard to find."

"But Father, how wouldst thou set about finding it? She putteth the evil eye on folk and she has dealings with the Devil. None dare enter her cottage, and she has a cat that is an evil spirit clothed in the flesh, and both o' them have nails like claws. We all run past her cottage."

Her father did not answer at once. Susan's question was a bit of a puzzle to him, for he too like George Fox himself, believed in witches. Did it not say in the Old Testament that witches should not live? At last he said, looking into the anxious face of his daughter:

"One thing, Susan, I know now for a surety. There is a Light of God, an Indwelling Spirit, in Mollie as in thee and me. It can never be wholly extinguished. It is when we show love to our neighbors, Susan, that their light is made manifest to us."

Susan found this answer hard to understand. She was a practical girl who liked clear directions.

Some time later when their parents had gone away again, she found Tom in the kitchen puzzling over some figures. There were no schools for ordinary children in those days. Susan had been busy all day washing clothes and cooking. She had baked Tom a huge plum pie, and had whipped cream for his supper, because it was his birthday.

"Tom," she said, "Didst understand what Father meant about Owd Mollie and standing i' the Light? It be so difficult."

Tom looked up into the flushed, puzzled face of his little sister and laughed. "Thee's not thinking o' tackling Mollie, Sue? The owd hag'll have her claws i' thee afore time to say Jack Robinson."

"But what did Father mean?" pursued Susan, who had a way of sticking to her point, "put in plain words?"

"Well," said Tom slowly, "I'd say he meant, treat folk, even witches, as if they are good, even though they bain't, and stick to it. He meant we've got to hunt for good as we do for treasure. But witches bain't for thee, Sue," he added a little anxiously, "thee'd best start off wi' summat easier."

This at any rate was plain English. Susan went to bed and thought about it. What ought she to do? Her father must be right, he always was. Yet the vicar and everybody else said witches were black right through, and Owd Mollie was a witch.

Susan was a determined girl and now she made a decision. She herself would try to prove which one was right, her father or the parson. She would try to find out whether Mollie had this spark of good in her. It would be a dangerous experiment, she knew, for witches had terrible power. Susan sank into sleep, and dreamed of flying on a broomstick up to the top of the great elm tree at the back of the smithy, where, all mixed up with the branches, she found the horns and hoof of a great red and black devil. Perhaps she had eaten too much plum pie and cream.

Every Wednesday it was Susan's task to take the week's supply of eggs to the Hall. Her path lay by the witch's cottage which was on the border of a wood a little way out of the village. Today on the way back Susan stopped at the rickety fence and looked around for Mollie. She wasn't there.

"Mollie, Mollie," she called, at first fearfully, and then more loudly. The gray cat came out, and seeing Susan ran back mewing to summon his mistress. Out she came, and, believing Susan to be one of the tormenting children who threw stones at her, she rushed at her screaming and cursing. Susan was shaking with fright, but she murmured to herself; "'Tis there, the spark o' God, 'tis there." She stood firm and, smiling at Mollie, held out her basket.

"Here be some scones for thee, Mollie. Can I have the basket back?"

The old witch peered at her with puzzled, suspicious eyes under her untidy gray locks. Then, as if certain it was all a trick, she snatched the basket with her clawlike fingers, and ran back to the house, chortling and chuckling, the cat following after her. At the door she turned, shook her fist and shouted: "Get it back, will ee? Get it back!" and disappeared.

Susan went home crestfallen. What would her mother say about the basket?

That evening Susan found that Tom had all but let the fire out. Indeed it looked quite out, and only when she had blown and blown with the bellows for a long time on the gray ash, did a spark show itself, then another and another and finally a little flame. Susan scattered on some

small wood, blew again, and quickly a warm fire was burning. As she hung the bellows on their nail and stretched
out her cold toes to the blaze, a thought jumped into her
head.

"Tom! Tom!" she cried excitedly. "This be like Owd
Mollie and me. She be the fire that looks dead, and I be
the bellows, or trying to be."

Tom smiled at her. "Bellows be summat I ought to know
about, for I've mended many a pair. If thou be bellows,
Sue, thou be best quality. Thou art a wise little woman wi'
thy parables." And he patted her head. Susan might bake
and mend for him but she was always his "little sister."

On the next Wednesday Susan met Old Mollie coming
out of the wood where she had evidently been gathering
herbs.

"Good day, Mollie," she said. "Would thee like some
more cakes?"

Mollie seized the scones hungrily and made a vain
snatch at the basket. Susan smiled at her and walked on.
As she reached the gate into the wood and turned to shut it,
she saw old Mollie still standing there, staring after her
with a puzzled look like a wild animal which fears to be
caught.

The next week Susan took a loaf of bread and some thick
soup. Mollie was again indoors, but Susan saw her face at
the window and guessed she was waiting for her. This in
itself was a step forward, and, when Mollie ran out at once
and stood a few yards off eyeing her doubtfully, Susan took
courage and said; "Don't be afraid o' me, Mollie. I won't
do thee any harm, I won't indeed. Here be a loaf for thee."

Old Mollie rushed forward, grabbed it, and started to run
indoors.

"Mollie, Mollie," called Susan, holding up the basin,
"Come back and I'll give thee this."

Mollie came back doubtfully. "It's like taming a wild bird," thought Susan.

"Look, Mollie, here be some thick soup. I made it for thee myself."

Now it's not so easy to snatch at a smooth basin as at a rough loaf, and Old Mollie's long-nailed, dirty hands closed over Susan's. You and I can hardly understand the shudder that came over Susan, for we live in days when witches are regarded as just make-believe. But to Susan Mollie was a wicked witch whose old hands had done dreadful things. Had they not concocted poisons and spells, and helped other witches to make clay or wax figures of their enemies, into which they had stuck pins, so that their enemies wasted away in terrible pain? It was horrible to have those evil hands so close to her.

But Susan held her ground. "Think only of her spark of good, don't think of her badness. Blow, blow."

"Can I have the basin back, please? I'll wait for it," she said smiling.

Just then the gray cat which followed Mollie about everywhere, and which, unseen by Susan, was close at her heels, brushed suddenly against her dress. Susan gave a cry of fear. "Get away! Get away!" she cried, stepping backwards.

The old woman's face changed. She uttered a sort of triumphant cackle as if to say, "Didn't I know all the time she was just like the rest and hated me and my cat!" and ran back into the cottage where she stayed looking out of the window shouting and waving her hands.

Poor Susan! By her show of fear had she undone all she had gained? It was true she feared the gray cat even more than Old Mollie, for a witch's cat was an evil spirit disguised—everyone knew that—and took messages from the Devil to the witches by night. Perhaps she herself would now come under the witch's curse, and fall ill or have an accident.

"I wish Father were at home," she thought, "and I could ask him whether there be a spark o' God in cats too. I think there must be. Our Griselda's such a nice friendly puss."

Susan went home crestfallen, but undefeated.

Perhaps the good taste of the soup went some way towards helping Old Mollie to forget Susan's treatment of her cat, for the next week she was again peering out of the window. Susan gave her more scones, asked her again for the basin, smiled at her when she shook her head and scowled; said "Nice pussy," to the cat, (that meant a real effort), and passed on.

The next week it was the same. Then came a clear spark from Susan's bellows. This time Mollie brought back the basin and in it was a packet of medicinal herbs, gathered from the woods.

"Tha be Ellen Abbott's girl," she muttered. "Th'art too young to want a love potion, but tell thy mother Mollie Robinson says these herbs'll cure the toothache, if they be steeped i' water."

It was a much longer speech than Susan had believed Mollie capable of. And how it rejoiced her! Why! Mollie was showing gratitude for the cakes, and gratitude was a good thing, Susan had been taught that. Did it not mean recognizing the good-will in somebody else? Here was a spark of God!

And Mollie had a surname! How odd it sounded! "Mollie Robinson!"

Susan smiled all over her face, thanked the old woman warmly for the medicine, and suddenly and impulsively stooped down and patted the gray cat.

A queer something passed over Old Mollie's face. Was

it a smile that crumpled up her dirty, wrinkled features? Or was it a grimace?

"Poor Molly," thought Susan. "'Tis so long since she's smiled that she's forgotten how." And suddenly all her efforts to believe that Mollie had the spark of God hidden away deep inside her, all the stress and strain of pretending she had, seemed to fall away, and instead she found herself feeling a warm affection for the old woman. She no longer wanted to run away. Her hand slipped through the fence and she patted Mollie's arm, saying: "Dear Mollie, th'art jannock, I know thou art." It was just the way she patted and talked to the old horse through the fence at home.

Mollie's face became more contorted than ever, and a tear splashed down her cheek. It startled Susan, but she went on patting and said comfortingly:

"Father says we all hae a spark o' good in us. He calls it Light from God. And now that thee's found thy spark, Mollie, thee needn't be a witch any more."

Again she had stumbled.

"I be a witch, I be, I be," cried Mollie excitedly. "Who says I b'aint a witch?"

Muttering imprecations she ran back to her cottage, the cat at her heels.

Susan tried hard to discover what she had said wrong. Surely Mollie didn't like being a witch. But perhaps she was afraid of offending the Devil, lest terrible harm come to her. It was all very difficult. But Susan took comfort from remembering that Mollie had tried to smile and really had cried. How could she make friends again with her?

She was to get more surprises. Making friends with Mollie was like taming a robin, at first so shy and suspicious, then growing bolder, then timid again, and then one day cocking his head at your very feet, or even sitting on the handle of the spade you are digging with. The next time she passed the witch's cottage there was Old Mollie waiting for her just behind the fence, and, having taken the food Susan had brought, she actually came out again with her poor shawl round her thin shoulders, and saying "Ah be goin' to the wood," she walked by Susan's side.

Susan's heart bounded with joy.

"Art thou a-hunting for roots, Mollie? I did hear a woman at market say that thy heart medicine is the best her husband knows. She'd come all the way from Lancaster for more o' it."

When she heard this such a transformation came over Mollie's face that Susan could only stare at her. She positively beamed for joy and for the moment looked strangely young.

"I do make them drugs good," she said simply. "Would 'ee like to see where I get them roots?" She added anxiously, "But 'ee won't tell a soul?"

Susan promised.

After that Mollie was always waiting for her to go into the wood and show her where to find certain plants. Indeed Mollie proved to be a most interesting companion, for she knew so much about the wild life in the woods and fields. Once she showed Susan where a squirrel was having his winter sleep.

"'Ee won't tell 'em wicked boys?" she asked first, and Susan promised.

*   *   *

So some weeks passed till it was December. Mollie had a bad cough and seemed to breathe with difficulty. Susan was afraid of her falling ill, and was longing for her mother to come back.

In Susan's days a girl of twelve was looked upon as older and more responsible than a girl of her age would be now, and quite able to run a house alone for a while. But Susan's parents had now been away for three months, and she was missing them badly.

Her joy was great, therefore, when, coming home from seeing Mollie, whose cough still sounded in her ears, she found her parents had returned.

That evening Susan told them all about Old Mollie, the lost basket, the basin, the walks in the wood, her calling herself 'Mollie Robinson' and particularly about her insistence on being a witch.

"Why dost tha think she wants to be a witch?" she asked sadly.

After a long silence it was her mother who answered her.

"I remember poor old Mollie when she must have been about forty and I was not yet thy age, Susan. She had a good and loving husband. Jake was his name, Jake Robinson, and she had a fine boy too. He must have been about sixteen when it happened. He used to play hopscotch with me. Then a terrible thing happened. Her husband and son were both lost in a great snowstorm, while they were out looking for sheep. They'd been buried for many days before they were found. And Mollie went crazy-like with grief, and would not stay at home. For weeks she wandered over the countryside, digging up the ground and trying to find them. She came home at last, but she's been queer ever since, with wild fits, spending half her time in the fields grubbing for herbs. She carried on so crazily sometimes that little by little people took to calling her a witch. Then Farmer Croft's son died of fits the very day after Mollie had cursed him for killing her cat, and that kind of fixed her in folks' mind as a witch. No one would give her work or buy her potions unless she threatened them with the evil eye and such works of the Devil."

After a pause she added, turning to Roger, "I have it heavily on my heart, Husband, that we village folk have not dealt kindly with poor Mollie Robinson." She sighed. "Alas! we lived not in the Light."

"Then let us thank God, Wife, that our Susan here has been making good where we failed," said Roger Abbott. And he patted Susan's head.

Susan's heart jumped for joy and relief. She had feared her mother might be annoyed at the lost basket, and at her talking to Mollie. And instead here was her father patting her on the head, and mother seemingly more grieved with herself than with Susan. Now Susan felt she wouldn't be afraid of a dozen witches.

When she set off next day, carrying not only food but a warm blanket that her mother had given her for Mollie, the first snowflakes of the year were beginning to fall. Susan, warmly cloaked and hooded, danced along.

This time she saw Mollie coming out of the wood. At once she felt there was something wrong. Mollie was wailing and waving her arms above her head, and hurrying along as if fleeing from something.

As she came up to Susan she gasped out:

"'Tis falling, 'tis falling. 'Twill cover 'em up. I must get my spade, or 'twill cover 'em up."

What was falling Susan did not at first understand, but it was clear that the poor old woman was in a frenzy of fear, and could hardly stagger along. Her voice was hoarse and she seemed to breathe with difficulty.

Susan had no hesitation now. She put her strong young arm round Mollie's waist to help her stumbling feet along. Mollie hardly seemed to notice her, and Susan found herself guiding her through the rickety gate, up to the very door of the hovel—through—in! Yes! right inside the home

of the vile old witch who had sold her soul to the Devil
and which none in the village dared to enter. And she
wasn't afraid at all!

It was a poor little room, with little in it but a heavy old
table, a rickety chair on the hearth, a broken-down old bed
and a milking stool. There was a strong smell of herbs
which hung in bunches from the rafters.

Susan guided Mollie to the chair where she sat muttering dazedly. Meanwhile she went round looking for the
bellows to blow up the dying fire. All of a sudden old
Mollie stood up and began frantically waving her arms over
her head as if keeping something away.

"What is it, Mollie?" asked Susan running back to her.
"What hae scared thee so?"

"'Tis the snow, the cruel snow," said Mollie wildly.
"'Tis covering them up."

Then to Susan's terror she crumpled up in a heap on
the floor. Susan half carried, half dragged her to the bed,
the gray cat mewing round her legs so that she nearly
stumbled. How light Mollie was! Then she rushed frantically to a cupboard in the wall hoping to find some milk.
There was a plate or two, a cracked cup, an old spoon and
knife, a basin, and absolutely nothing else.

"Mollie is starving," thought Susan, greatly relieved to
find a definite cause for the old woman's collapse.

She hurried to blow up the fire and heat some of the
broth she had brought. But when she put it to Mollie's
lips she would not drink. She did not seem to know her
but kept muttering and turning as though in a fever. The
cat jumped on to the bed miaowing distressfully.

"Pussy can't be hungry at any rate," said Susan to herself. "He's fat with the mice he catches. But he's anxious
for Mollie, and so am I."

Susan herself was terribly anxious. What ought she to

do? She must get help. She decided to run home and fetch her mother. She hated leaving Mollie alone, but something very bad was the matter with her and Susan couldn't manage by herself. Strangely enough it never occurred to her that Mollie, being a witch, might be possessed by the Devil and shaken by evil spirits. All these frightening thoughts of a few weeks ago were forgotten, and, as she ran as hard as she could the whole half-mile home, she thought of nothing but how to help the poor lonely old creature.

Things, however, had been happening at home while she was out. Susan's mother had had visitors.

It was not likely that in a country village Susan's dealings with the old witch had gone unnoticed. As the weeks went by, this person and that had seen her talking to Old Mollie over the fence, and even giving her presents, and getting things from her, too. The tongues of the gossips had wagged more and more furiously, and now three of Mistress Abbott's neighbors, learning that she was again at home, had come to tell her of Susan's wicked goings-on, and to reproach her for leaving her young daughter so long alone, an easy prey to the Devil and his followers.

They told their story with long faces and ominous shakings of their heads, expecting Susan's mother to show surprise and horror. But Ellen Abbott heard them to the end in silence, then she said:

"I am sure ye come with good-will to me and mine to tell me of this, and for that I thank ye all three. But I have already heard this story, though with differences, from my good little Susan, and I have sought help this night on the matter from God. Before I answer, I would like to ask ye some questions."

"Do ye remember Mary Robinson?"

There was a pause. It was so long since they had thought of 'Owd Mollie' as anything but the village witch that they had to jog their memories before they could connect her with Mistress Mary Robinson, one of the village matrons of their youth.

Then with question after question, little by little, Susan's mother recalled to them Mollie's sad history. She herself had spent much of the night thinking about it, and now her simple telling of the tragic history moved the hearts of her listeners.

She ended, "Standing in the Light of God, my friends, it has been borne in upon me that we have sinned against Mollie Robinson. We have not remembered the Master's story of the Good Samaritan."

"Who is Mollie's neighbor?" she asked them solemnly. "'He that doeth good to her,' saith Jesus." She looked at them in turn. "Has that been thee or me? No. It has been left to my little Susie to see the way."

"But Old Mollie saith herself she is a witch and hath sold her soul to the Devil," protested Mistress Bright, the eldest of the three.

"Hast thou reflected, Jane Bright, that only by threatening us with her witchcraft could Mollie get food? My friends, it hath been borne in upon me this night that maybe most so-called witches be just crazy folk who have lost their wits along of trouble. And if so be, some of them be truly possessed of devils, what example did our Master give us with such? He cast out the devils, and this not by their own powers of violence and fear and evil, but by the goodness that was in Himself, by the Power of God. And that same goodness, if only in small portion, is in each of us for the using. Have we used it to help Old Mollie?"

The three visitors were deeply impressed by Mistress Abbott's serious words. The long-forgotten name of Mary

Robinson stirred their memories and consciences. In silence they stood up to go.

It was just as this moment that Susan rushed in panting for breath, heedless of visitors or her own muddy feet.

"Oh, Mother, Mother, come at once, please, please come," she cried. "Old Mollie's very ill. She's starved—there's no food in the house—and she doesn't know me. I put her to bed, 'tis but straw and rags, and she won't eat, and she talks and talks about the snow coming down and covering them up and I've run all the way for thee, Mother." She gasped for breath. "Oh! poor, poor, poor old Mollie! And she's all alone."

Susan fell into a chair, and, still gasping for breath, broke into convulsive sobbing.

Perhaps nothing could have convinced the three visitors more completely of Susan's innocence of evil and of their own guilt than seeing her there crying her young heart out with pity for the woman they had failed to befriend.

Now it was all action.

"I've got an old mattress," said one. "By a lucky chance I brought it down to the fire only yesterday to air."

"I'll bring soap and scrubbing brushes," said another.

"I'll send my Bob off to get logs and kindling, and I've a feather pillow I can spare."

All of them hastened home, to turn up later at Mollie's cottage, not only with milk and butter and eggs and cordials, but with all kinds of useful things—crockery, pots and rugs, a warming pan and a large assortment of clothing.

*   *   *

Mollie's was a long illness. The neighbors took it in turns to sit up with her at nights, always two together, for when the wind blew and the old cottage shook, and Mollie tossed and muttered on her bed, they could not easily throw off their old belief that the place was haunted by evil spirits. But the great thing was that they *did* come at night and *did* find themselves unharmed when morning came.

All these strange faces might have frightened the old woman, but most of the time she was too ill to notice. Susan's mother, however, saw that, whenever the frightened look did come into her eyes, the sight of Susan always calmed her.

Slowly strength returned to her.

When Christmas Eve came, she was able to sit up in bed and eat her supper with some show of appetite. How different everything looked, thought Susan, who had come in for a while so that Mistress Green, whose turn it was, might finish plucking a goose.

The villagers' repentance had taken practical shape. They had almost refurnished Mollie's empty home. There was a comfortable chair by the fire, and the rickety bed and ragged bedclothes were no more. Mollie was dressed in a decent bedgown and white night-cap.

She was sitting up in bed, her eyes fastened, rapturously on the bunch of red-berried holly that Susan had put on the table.

"It be Christmas Eve, Mollie, so I've brought thee some holly."

Mollie sat looking at it, then she said:

"Ah mind the last Christmas that Jake were here. We did fill the place wi' berries. Jake liked 'em."

"Dear Mollie," said Susan. "The cottage will always look cosy now. And Pussy's so happy. Bain't thee happy, Puss?"

The cat, hearing himself called, left the hearth and jumped on the bed.

"My pussykins," sighed Mollie, hugging him. "Tha loved me when . . ."

Just then the distant chimes broke out. The ringers were practising for Christmas Day. Mollie lay back, the cat in her arms and Susan beside her, looking strangely happy and peaceful. Susan could hardly believe this was the wild, tormented 'Owd Mollie' of a few weeks ago.

Suddenly Mollie said, "Tha be my friend, Susan? Ah be good now." There was a long pause. Then she added: "Perhaps ah never were a witch. Ah can't remember."

"Don' thee try to remember, Mollie. Of course I be thy friend, and so be Mother, and Father be coming to see thee tomorrow, and thou hast lots o' friends now in the village, Mollie. We be all going to take care o' thee."

Mollie lay back listening to the bells.

Just then there came the sound of shuffling feet outside, lanterns flashed, and out broke the voices of children singing "The First Noel".

"They be come all along to sing to me," said Mollie happily.

After a pause she began murmuring the words, trying to recall the carol she had once known well—"Certain poor shepherds . . . keeping their sheep . . . on a cold winter's night that was so deep." Another pause . . . "so deep" she repeated . . . there was a longer pause.

Then she said softly, "Ma husband . . . Jake . . . he were a shepherd, Susan. And ma boy, Robbie, he were going to be one, too." A pause . . . "Ah thought they were out i' the cold cold ground—ah couldna' win 'em back . . . but now they be here wi' me in this warm room, here a cherishing o' me, here in my heart. Thou hast brought 'em back to me, Susan."

A North Country story by Caroline C. Graveson

THE SILVER PESO

As THE SUN disappeared over the low green hills and the chill of evening settled in the valley, Josef walked faster along the dusty road that led to San Gabriel Mission. In those early days, a hundred years ago in California, when there were few white men in the land, brave padres, or priests of the Catholic Church, had built these Missions in the wilderness. Here the padres taught the Indians about God and how to do useful things such as weaving cloth and raising wheat. Besides taking the place of churches, schools and workshops, the Missions served as free hotels to any travellers who might be journeying up or down the coast.

Josef, as he thought of the huge crackling fire of logs and the steaming hot supper a little way ahead, should have been cheerful and happy. He was young and strong and was not tired with walking. The evening was clear and lovely. A mocking bird sang himself to sleep in a palm tree by the road. But Josef's face was gloomy. One hand thrust deep into his trousers pocket clutched his last peso, a silver coin worth about a dollar. The feel of it made him angry. It was all he had in the world except a little bundle of clothes under his arm.

That year Josef had had bad luck. He had owned a fine herd of cattle that spent the summer browsing on the short grass of the hills. He had gone into the mountains to look for gold and when he returned his cattle were lost, probably chased far away by wolves. Neither had he found the gold, though other men told him it lay buried in the rocks of the great mountains. Bitter and discouraged, he had started to walk south into Mexico, all his money spent except one silver peso.

As Josef walked along, a wicked idea was shaping itself in his mind. He knew that in the church of the Mission were four beautiful silver candlesticks brought all the way across the water from Spain. Slender candles were kept always burning in them. He said to himself, "I will steal a candlestick in the night and carry it under my coat down into Mexico, where I will sell it. Then I will have more money to put with my one peso."

Across the fields came the sound of the Mission bells calling the Indians to evening prayers. In a few minutes Josef sat before the fire, the good Padre himself smiling a greeting. No man was asked at the Mission who he was or why he had come, for each was welcome, in the name of God, to meals, a bed and whatever he needed for his comfort.

Others travellers gathered around the blaze, but Josef sat apart, eating the beans and bread brought to him by a little Indian boy. All but he were cheerful and merry as they questioned the Padre about the Indians under his care and the fine gardens and fields of the Mission. At last Josef rose and silently tiptoed to the door of the church. There, before a picture of the Christ Child in his mother's arms, burned the four candles in their silver candlesticks.

Josef returned to the fire, muttering, "I wish to sleep now." The Padre bowed his head, and answered, "May God bless thy slumbers. The boy will show thee thy room."

When the little Indian had lighted him to the tiny room and he was alone, he looked around carefully to discover whether it would be possible to escape quietly in the night with the candlestick. Nothing could be easier, for the room was without a door and opened out on the grass-plot behind the church. Within the room the only furniture was a bed and a small table. On the table stood a bowl of the rough kind of pottery made by the Indians.

As Josef set the candle down on the table the light gleamed on something bright. He looked closer and was amazed to find the bowl half filled with copper and silver coins. His first thought was that the last man who had slept in the room had put this money on the table and then forgotten it. He started eagerly to pour the coins into his pocket, but they made such a jangling that he was frightened. He thought the Padre might hear, and of course would immediately take possesion of all his wealth. As he handled the treasure very softly he noticed letters scratched in the sides of the bowl. Holding it close to the light, he read:

"Let him who stands in greatest need take from this bowl and go forth in peace."

Josef read these words over and over before he realized their meaning. The money was kept there so that any guest who was very poor might help himself. No one had counted it before he, Josef, had come, and no one would count it after he departed. He might take only one small copper—or none—or the entire bowlful, and still he was free to go away with the Padre's blessing, having received a night's lodging, good food and money—and himself given nothing.

For a long time Josef sat on the bed and thought about this. There was no reason why he should not put the money with the one peso already in his pocket—and perhaps take the candlestick besides. His need was certainly great. Had he not lost all his cattle, failed to find the gold, and stood now without a thing in the world except one coin and a few clothes? The Padre had meant it for such as he. As for the candlestick—well, he would leave the candlestick. It was wicked to steal from the church. He was young and strong and could find work easily. He would only take part of the money from the bowl. But first he would sleep.

Josef lay on his back, wide awake and quiet. Since he had decided not to steal the candlestick he felt as though a load had been lifted from his heart. He stroked the great muscles of his arms and thought, "How strong I am!" The words on the bowl, "Who stands in greatest need," kept running through his head. After all, with strength like his, why should he take the Padre's money? Others would need it more.

He turned over and closed his eyes, but the face of the good Padre came continually before him.

Suddenly Josef leaped from his bed. He searched hurriedly in his trousers pocket for the one silver peso and dropped it with a loud clink into the bowl. It would be for those whose need was greater than his. With a smile he lay down again and fell asleep.

Anna D. White

THE ROAD TO CANADA

For two hours Allen had been keeping watch in the peach orchard near the road. He was a Quaker boy who lived in Ohio in the days when there were still Negro slaves in part of the United States. The Friends thought it a wicked thing to buy and sell men and women as though they were cows and horses, and many Friends were willing to run great risks in order to help slaves to their freedom. If any slave could escape from his owner, cross the river into Ohio, and reach the home of any such Friends, he would be helped by them from one place to another across the State, and into Canada, where he would be free. Even if his master were close behind him, and knew exactly where he had gone, he would seem to disappear. People came to say that the Quakers and the other abolitionists sent the slaves by an "Underground Railroad".

Allen was only eleven years old, but he knew that his own home was a station on the "Railway." Sometimes, he had seen a Negro man or woman come in, tired and hungry; sometimes, he knew, they came in the night, and went on again, before he was up in the morning. His father and mother never told him how they came, or where they went. It was enough to know that they had been slaves, and were going to be free.

Today, he himself was part of the "Railway," and he felt very proud, as he looked down the road to the southward. That morning his father had said to him, "Allen, I am going to the far field to work. If any Negro should come along, thee can take him down to the cornfield, if thee likes, and hide him under the big walnut tree. But

56

do not tell me about it, or thy mother, or anybody else."

And so Allen played by the roadside, and watched for the runaway slave who might come along. And sure enough, there at last came a poor fellow, with ragged clothes and feet bleeding from the rough roads that he had gone over and the underbrush he had broken through on his way to freedom. Hurrying along with all speed, he turned, every now and then, to listen, and then hurried on again even faster than before.

Allen ran out into the road to meet him. The man started in terror, at sight even of the boy, and looked from side to side, as for a hiding-place. Allen spoke quickly.

"Is there somebody after thee?" he said. "I'll hide thee, so that they can not find thee."

"Yo' will? Can yo', for shuah? Is yo' Mistah Jay's boy?" Allen nodded. The Negro grinned.

"Dey tole me dat I'd get help heah. I'll go just wheah yo' says."

Allen quickly led the way among the trees of the orchard. When they were out of sight of the road, the Negro looked back, and sighed with relief. Beyond the orchard was the big cornfield, with rows of corn standing higher than a man's head.

"Nobody can find thee here," said Allen.

"Deed they can't," answered the slave. "I feels perfectly safe now."

Farther and farther in among the rows of corn they went, until at last the great walnut-tree was reached, its branches spreading wide in every direction.

"Now, thee stay right here," said Allen, "and wait for me. I will come for thee at the right time."

"I won't stir from heah," answered the man. "I'se been walkin' all day yest'day, an' all night, an' I'se tired 'nuff to sleep till tomorrow comes, ef I only wasn't so hungry."

"I will get thee something to eat," answered the boy, as he started back to the house.

He intended to go to the pantry and help himself to some food for the fugitive. But when he reached the kitchen, he found his mother busy spreading slices of bread with butter, and laying cold meat between. She looked up as he entered and smiled, but said nothing, and Allen sat down and watched, as she packed a basket with the sandwiches, cake, and fruit. Then she filled a jug with rich, creamy milk, and turned to him.

"Allen, if thee knows of anybody who thee thinks is hungry, thee might take this basket to him."

Allen could hardly restrain his eagerness, as he slipped off his chair, and seized the basket and jug. But he was amused, too, and he answered with the slightest touch of a smile. "I will try to find somebody; but if I do not, I may eat the lunch myself."

"Very well," answered his mother, seriously, and Allen hurried out across the back yard, and over the fields to the great walnut tree, where the colored man lay resting his weary limbs and watching hungrily for the boy's return.

The man ate as though starved, and there was little left in the basket when he at last paused and poured out his thanks to Allen.

"I can sleep now," he said. "I hasn't had my stomach full since I lef' ol' Virginny." As Allen turned away, the man stretched himself out on the ground, and seemed to fall asleep immediately.

Allen returned to the house, and to his own dinner. His father and mother chatted as usual, but the boy was unusually silent. He was thinking about the Negro lying under the walnut tree, and wondering if he would get safely to Canada. That there were people who would do all they could to prevent this, he was soon to learn; for the family were still at the table, when two or three rough-looking men came riding up to the gate, and called loudly to Mr. Jay to come out. Very politely, he obeyed their call, saying only, as he left the room:

"They look like slave-catchers. I suppose they are searching for some unfortunate escaped Negro. Even if I had one sitting here at the dinner-table, I would never give him up."

The Jay house stood rather near the road. Allen slipped into the "front room" and stood out of sight beside an open window where he could hear all that was said by the men on horseback, and by his quiet, self-contained father.

"Have you seen a nigger going by here today?" was the first question.

"No, I have not," came the reply.

"Don't you let him fool you, Jim," interrupted the other rider. "The nigger didn't go past, because he came in. Look here, you Quaker, that nigger's in your house, and we're going to look for him there."

"There is no Negro in my house, but if it will give you pleasure to look for him, you are at liberty to do so, provided that you have the proper authority."

But this they did not have. They could only bluster and threaten, and finally ride away in disgust.

The afternoon passed as usual. Suppertime came and it began to grow dark. Allen wondered more and more what was to be done with the man. Surely, he was not to be left under the tree all night. And then at last his father spoke.

"Allen, I have a basket of apples to send to thy grandfather. It is getting a little dark, but I think thee can drive over with old Ned, can thee not?"

"Yes, indeed," answered the boy eagerly.

"I will harness the horse for thee, and put the apples in

the wagon. It is only five miles, of course, but if thee would like to take anybody along, I shall be glad to have thee do so."

"Thank thee, father," said Allen quietly, as became his father's son. Catching up his cap, he ran out at the kitchen door, and across the back yard toward the walnut tree. The Negro was still sleeping, but Allen caught him by the shoulder, and quickly roused him to the need of continued flight.

"Come," he said. "We're going on."

The man sprang to his feet, caught up the basket with its remains of lunch, and followed the boy to the barn-yard. There stood old Ned, harnessed and tied to a tree, his head toward the road. Everything was ready for the start, but Mr. Jay was nowhere to be seen, and Allen knew that he was to drive away without further words.

It was now quite dark, but Ned, a wise and experienced old horse, knew the road even better than Allen, and trotted along at his own moderate pace. They met few people, and had no adventures of any kind, before reaching the home of Allen's grandfather. Half an hour after their arrival, the Negro was astride a good horse, and trotting northward, with another friendly Quaker beside him, on his way to the next "station" of the Underground Railroad.

Anna L. Curtis

JANE ADDAMS'S BURGLARS

To THE newcomer in Halstead Street, the Lady of Hull House must have seemed to be very rich. She lived in a beautiful house in the midst of beautiful furnishings. The neighbors who inhabited the shabby houses and tenements which surrounded Hull House on every side knew well that Jane Addams had restored this old dwelling and brought together these beautiful things in order to have a welcoming place for any who needed friends and neighbors. They knew that she kept nothing for herself. When money was given to her she spent it in a way to help as many people as possible. But it is not surprising that there were a few people who thought that because Jane Addams lived in this beautiful place she must be very wealthy, and who wanted for themselves the money which they thought she had.

It must have been one of these who climbed in through her window on the second floor one night and woke her while he was rummaging about. At that time her little nephew lived with her, as he had done since his mother died, and he was sleeping in the next room.

Jane Addams's first thought was that the intruder might wake the little boy and so she said to him in her calm pleasant voice,

"Don't make a noise!"

She was not frightened, but the burglar was. He rushed to the window to climb out and get away before he was caught.

Jane Addams said to him as she might have said to her nephew, "Don't go down that way. You might hurt yourself. Go out in the hall and walk down the stairway!"

The man obeyed her. She heard him hurry down the stairway and out of the door and then everything was quiet. The child had not been wakened; the burglar had not been hurt.

It was some years later that she woke again one night to hear some one moving around her room.

She sat up in bed. "What do you want?" she inquired of the darkness.

"I want money, Miss Addams," a man's voice answered gruffly.

"Oh, you know me, do you?" she asked with interest. She did not recognize his voice. She knew a great many people, but still more people knew Jane Addams.

"Yes," the man said.

"What is the trouble?"

"I need money," the man told her. "I'm out of work."

"I don't have any money," Jane Addams said. It was impossible not to believe her. "But if you will come around to the office at nine in the morning I'll try to find a job for you."

The man hesitated, but he could not resist her friendly reasonable voice. He left her room without more ado, and in the morning he came to the office and told her who he was, and she found work for him as she had promised.

If Jane Addams had kept hidden in her room the large sum of money that these men thought they might find there, probably she could not have taken their unexpected visits so calmly. Since she possessed nothing that her friends could not share, and since she was interested first of all in the welfare of other people, even burglars, she was better protected than she could have been by bolts and chains and double-locks.

THE SEVEN KINGDOMS
AND THE HIDDEN SPRING

THERE was once a large island in a distant ocean, so large that it was divided into seven kingdoms, over which reigned seven kings. The island was nearly round, and the boundaries between the kingdoms ran from the sea-shore toward the center, like the spokes of a wheel; and on each boundary was a high stone wall. So the seven stone walls met at a spot in the central highlands of the interior.

On every side of the island was the great blue ocean, full of all manner of fish, and the climate was so friendly that the place was never troubled with storms. Each of the seven kingdoms had a harbor, into which ships from far-off lands might come, bringing whatever the people needed which the island did not provide. One would have said that these needs amounted to almost nothing, since the island was so large and provided with almost every kind of good soil; and this would have been true were it not for one strange misfortune which brought all kinds of other misfortunes in its train, so that the seven kingdoms, instead of being among the happiest in the world, bade fair to be among the most miserable.

This strange thing was that the island had no water, except, of course, the salt water of the sea. There were no rivers nor lakes; the climate was so unceasingly fair that it never rained; and the mountains were not high enough to be capped with snow. Every one knew that there must really be fresh water in the island, since there were trees and shrubs, which in some way must find it by their roots.

But no one had even come upon any flowing from the ground, nor had any one been able to dig a well deep enough to discover it. So the people of the seven kingdoms had either to buy their water of those who brought it in ships from distant countries, or to distil it, by slow and expensive processes, from the salt water of the sea. Consequently they never had all they wanted; or, if any one had been able to buy enough for himself, he was considered the richest person in the land, and was envied by all the rest.

Now there was an old legend or tradition that the water under the island had once flowed out through a great spring, and had been amply sufficient for the seven kingdoms, but that at some time the spring had become filled up or been lost. You may imagine that each of the seven Kings hoped that it might again be found within the limits of his own kingdom, and set all his energies to the task of searching for it. The wise men of each court were commanded to have at least one meeting every month, to study the subject of the lost spring; and whenever any of them thought he had discovered anything hopeful, no time nor money was spared to carry out his ideas. But for many long years there had been no results at all.

If there had been nothing worse than the scarcity of water, it would have been bad enough. But worse trouble had come after. The Kings had grown very jealous of one another, and so had all their subjects, lest the spring be found in one kingdom, and, not being sufficient to supply them all, should put the rest at a disadvantage. So whenever any of them thought that he was on the track of water, he would try to keep it secret from all the rest; and on the other hand spies were sent from one kingdom into another, to try to learn what was going on there. There was the same jealousy regarding water brought from foreign ships; and the Kings strengthened the walls along their boundaries, and set guards upon them, so that no one should sell any water to the people in a less fortunate kingdom. If the digging of a well was begun anywhere near one of these boundary walls, the people in the adjoining kingdom were certain to begin digging close to the wall on their side also: then, before long, there would be more jealousy and strife. For one or the other king would complain that the digging was too near his wall, and might injure it if they went deeper; and the diggers themselves would shout threats and insults to one another over the wall. Often these threats and insults would be followed by stones. So sometimes a real battle, or even a prolonged war, would result from these occasions; and nearly always the digging of the well was stopped, before it had gone very far, in order that the diggers might join in the fighting.

The worst conflicts occurred, as you may easily believe, at the center of the island, where the seven walls came together, and guards from all seven kingdoms were stationed to watch against misdeeds on the part of their rivals. It was natural that here, among the mountains, there should be more hope than elsewhere of finding the hidden spring, but also more difficulty in digging secretly or without arousing the fears of others. So there was a long and bloody history of battles at the meeting-place of the seven walls, and I have heard it said that the bones of fallen soldiers were piled as high, in the angles of the walls, as the building-stones themselves.

Now at length there was born, in one of the seven kingdoms, a child named Philoxenus, who became a student, so that even when he was still a boy he was known as one likely to be a wise man. And as Philoxenus dearly loved his country and his fellow-countrymen, he very early resolved to devote himself to the great subject of the water supply. First he studied all that was known about the nature of water, and the means of digging for it and pumping it; but he soon found, of course, that the wise men of the kingdom knew all this, and more. Then he resolved to find what was known in the other kingdoms, and set out to travel through them. Here, however, he found great difficulty; for the seven Kings and their subjects now hated one another so bitterly that men were not allowed to pass from one kingdom to another, unless their business was very urgent. Philoxenus finally obtained a pass from his King, who was interested in the boy's studies, but who warned him that he would be in danger of being put to death by an enemy before he had gone far on his journey. Nevertheless Philoxenus set out, and his manner was so friendly and his purpose so earnest that he made his way through all the seven kingdoms, and was at home again by the end of the year.

The most surprising thing that Philoxenus learned from this journey was that the people of all the kingdoms were remarkably alike. He had heard such dreadful things about them, because of the long and bitter wars, that he was astonished to find them on the whole very much like those of his own kingdom. Certainly they all needed water equally badly, and knew exactly as much about getting it —which was nothing at all. When the King heard of Philoxenus's return, he sent for him to report what he had seen, and the boy told him everything. At the end he told him that he thought all the seven kingdoms were much alike, and needed water equally badly; but at this the King frowned, and said, "You must not talk like that, or you may be sent to prison."

So Philoxenus did not say it to any one else, but went back to his studies.

Then he took up history because he wanted to find all that he could about the sufferings of his people, and the further he went among the ancient records, the surer he became that it was true that the seven kingdoms had once had a spring of water, sufficient for them all. And when history could not tell him any more, he began to study philosophy, which is about why-everything-is-so. Now the greatest philosopher in the kingdom was a very old man, who was so wise that some thought him a magician, and who had in his keeping the oldest and most precious of the ancient books. Philoxenus went to him and asked whether, if he studied long enough, he might be able to read in the Great Book.

"It is not a question of studying long enough," said the old man. "It is whether you believe what you find in it. As soon as I think you are the sort of person to do that, I will give it to you."

Then Philoxenus told him why he wished to study the Book, and what he had already learned. When the old man had heard all that the boy had to say, he said, "You may have the Great Book. Read one page a day, for six days; on the seventh return to me."

Now the first page that Philoxenus turned to contained only seven words. They were these:

"What one can not, two can do."

So that day he read no more, but thought of what he had found. And the second day he turned a leaf and read:

"What two can not, three can do."

And on the third day he read:

"What three can not, four can do."

And on the fourth day:

"What four can not, five can do."

And on the fifth day:

"What five can not, six can do."

And on the sixth day:

"What six can not, seven can do."

On the seventh day Philoxenus went to the old philosopher, and said, "I think I understand. I am going to tell the King, and ask him to call the other six Kings together."

The old man smiled. "You may ask him," he said. "But that is all the good it will do."

"But will he not believe the Great Book?" asked Philoxenus.

"If he does," said the old man, "there is another thing he had better hear. Go back, before you speak to the King, and read one page more."

Then Philoxenus went back to the Great Book and read the seventh page. It said:

"One for all, and all for each."

After that he went to the King, and told him that in order to find the hidden spring he felt certain the seven kingdoms must work together, and when they found it, be ready to share it with one another.

"But suppose it should be wholly within our own kingdom," said the King; "why in the world should we share it with others?"

"I am not sure that I know all the reasons," said Philoxenus. "But I will give two or three. One is what I told you before, that the other kingdoms need the water as much as we. Another is that if the spring should be found in one of them we should like to have them share it with us. But the principal reason is, that all my study of history leads me to think that the reason the spring was lost in the first place is that the kingdoms did not follow the teaching of the Great Book."

Now the King was by this time becoming fond of Philoxenus, and also was beginning to think that the boy had wisdom even if he was still young. So he said:

"I will call my counselors together, and tell them what you say."

When the counselors came together and were told about the Great Book and about Philoxenus, at first they were very angry. They said that they and all their countrymen had been fighting for years in order to keep the spring from belonging to any one else, and they could not now be traitors to their own kingdom.

"But you have never found the spring for us," said the King.

Perhaps they would not have yielded if it had not been such a terribly hard year. Less than the usual amount of water had come in foreign ships, and some parts of the kingdom were actually suffering for lack of it. So the counselors felt in the end that anything would be better than to do nothing, and they consented that the King should invite the other six kingdoms to unite in the search for the spring.

It would be a long story if I should tell of the excitement which the King's letter stirred up in the other kingdoms. At first it seemed as if it might be only the beginning of a worse war than any they had had before. To give up all their fighting over the question of water was hard enough; but it was still harder to promise that whoever found the spring would share it with the rest. Some of them sent word that they would try the first proposal, but not promise to follow the second.

"Then," said Philoxenus to the seven Kings, "you might as well not come together at all; for the finding of the water would only bring more hatred and more war."

At last they all saw that this was true, and agreed to his plan.

What, then, should they do first to carry on the search? By this time every one turned naturally to Philoxenus for guidance, and he was ready with an answer.

"We have always supposed," he said, "that the most

likely place for the spring is in the center of the island, and there is where all our kingdoms join and our walls come together. Let us break away the walls at the place where they meet, and look there for the hidden spring."

This again caused no little commotion, for some of the Kings objected strongly to tearing down any part of their walls of defense. What was to prevent their enemies from breaking through at once?

"But when we are all digging together," said Philoxenus, "there will not be any enemies. And if we fail, the walls can be repaired again."

So at last, with a good deal of grumbling, they consented; and each King sent a force of workmen, armed with picks and crowbars and hammers and wedges, to break down the extreme inner end of his wall. Before they could begin this work they had first to clear away the great piles of bones and old weapons which for years and years had been piling up at the center of the island, as a result of the fighting. When this was done, they attacked the walls themselves, and at last each of them was sufficiently broken to make an open space where the workmen of each of the Kingdoms could look through and see those of the other six. And just as Philoxenus had been surprised when he made his journey through the island, so all these men were surprised when they saw that their various enemies looked so little different from themselves.

There was now, to be sure, an open space at the center of the island, but it was filled, far below the level of the ground, with solid stone and cement, where the foundations of the seven walls had come together and been made deep and solid. How should they ever begin digging for water in such a place?

"There must be no stopping till we get to the earth itself," said Philoxenus. "Let the workmen bring blasting powder, and blow these obstructions away."

The seven Kings gave their consent, and each contributed some blasting powder, which was put into holes drilled deep in the stone. Then all the workmen and the onlookers drew back, while the fuses were lighted, and every one within sight or hearing of the place waited with excitement for the explosion.

Among them all I suppose no one was quite so excited as Philoxenus. It was he who had persuaded them to do this, and who believed more fully than any one else that they would succeed. Moreover, he had come so to hate the dividing walls which separated the seven kingdoms, that he said to himself, "This is the greatest day I have ever seen, even if we are no nearer to finding water than before, provided those foundations can be knocked into so many pieces that they can never be rebuilt."

It was indeed the greatest day he had ever seen. The fuse fired the powder, and the explosion shook the earth for miles around, while the air was filled with broken rock and cement from the old foundations. And the noise of this had not died down when from all the watchers there came shouts—"Look! Look!"—and their eyes almost burst from their heads as they stared at the place where a way had been cleared to the earth beneath. For there, in the midst of the wreckage, there rose high into the air a column of water, pure and glistening in the sunlight, and gurgling and splashing with joy in its freedom from its long imprisonment.

At first, I say, it rose high in air with the force of its sudden escape. Then it drooped, and fell over upon itself like a fountain, and so continued flowing and splashing, while all the people drew near and made sure that it was really fresh water; those who were close enough filled cups, or the palms of their hands, or their upturned hats, or whatever they could call into service, to carry away a little of the precious liquid.

It was noticed at once, by those most observing, that the spring flowed so exactly from the center of the island that no one of the Kings could say it was in his kingdom rather than in any of the other six. So there was no jealousy, and they did not even have to remember their promise to share the water when it had been found.

But there was one disappointment. The people supposed that the water would overflow from the spring and run in streams to the lower levels at some distance from the place where it had burst forth. But this was not the case. Despite the great abundance of the flow, hardly a drop escaped from the central spring. When Philoxenus noticed this, it set him thinking. "The water must go somewhere," he said to himself; "it cannot stand still. It must, then, be flowing where we cannot see it."

When he had thought a little further, he told his thoughts to the seven Kings, and asked them to command the workmen to break away somewhat more of the walls, and, if necessary, to blast out still more of the foundation stone, that they might learn what became of the water. "For," said he, "it may make a great difference to all the kingdoms if we do not have to carry it long distances from the central spring."

So the Kings gave orders as he requested, and the seven walls were broken down for some distance from the spring. The result was a great surprise to every one—except, perhaps, Philoxenus. For as soon as they got near to the bottom of the first wall, the workmen heard a rushing sound; and when they had cleared away all the rock and mortar, they saw a deep channel underneath, disappearing beneath the end of the wall which remained; and in it was a beautiful stream of water hurrying away from the spring. This

excited the other workmen to break through their foundations all the more quickly; and sure enough! in each case
the same thing appeared. Under each of the walls was a
deep pure stream, flowing from the spring toward the outer
parts of the island.

Then they broke down more and more of the walls, and
blasted out more and more of the foundation stones. And
always, as far as they went, they found under each of the
seven the same faithfully flowing stream.

"What does it mean?" said the Kings to Philoxenus.
"How has the water found passage exactly under our seven
walls?"

"I will tell you what it means," said the boy. "It means
that long ago the boundaries between these seven kingdoms
were seven beautiful streams, by which the waters of the
great spring found their way through the island to the
ocean. But gradually the Kings desired to fortify their
territory more strongly, and so built greater and greater
walls—at first by the side of the stream, then across it; and
at last, I suppose, the mass of stone and mortar covered
up the channel altogether, till in time no one was left who
even remembered its existence. But all these centuries the
spring has continued to flow under the rubbish with which
men covered it, and the seven streams have continued to
make their way to the sea."

"In that case," said the Kings, "if we tear away the walls
altogether, we shall have water for each of our kingdoms,
all the way from the center of the island to the coast."

"I have no doubt of it," said Philoxenus.

So the work went on. It was no small task to destroy
those great walls, from one end to the other, which had
been building for hundreds of years. But the people of all
the kingdoms worked with a will, and there came a day
when each one of the seven streams flowed all the way to

the sea under the open sky, with the water freely in reach of every one on either side. I cannot begin to tell how many happy things followed—how the flowers and ferns grew up along the banks, how birds came who had formerly shunned the island, how the people grew more cheerful in all the kingdoms, till you would not have known them for the same who used to live there.

It is true that not every one was pleased. Some of the Kings' men who had long been in charge of the great walls were dissatisfied because they had lost their employment, and a number of old people predicted all kinds of trouble because it was now so easy to pass from one kingdom to another, into an enemy's land. But the younger ones soon forgot that the region across the stream was an enemy's land, and even a few of the older ones learned that, to love their own kingdom, they had no need to hate any other.

As for Philoxenus, he grew to be the chief wise man, and in his old age had charge of the Great Book in which he had studied as a boy. And when he died, they made a great statue of him, close to the central spring, and carved on its base the words he had so often quoted to them from the Book: "One for all, and all for each."

Meantime the spring flowed faithfully on, and so did the seven streams. And I suppose the time would have come when it had been forgotten that the island ever lacked water, except that the seven Kings had the story written in the Great Book of each kingdom, in order that no one might ever again seek to build the walls that they had torn down.

From The Boy Who Found the King, *by Raymond MacDonald Alden. Copyright, 1922. Used by special permission of the publisher, The Bobbs-Merrill Company.*

ADVERTISING FOR A THIEF

BETTY always loved rainy days when she was visiting at her grandfather's. Because for rainy days she saved the greatest treat of all the wonderful things there were to do in this country paradise. It was playing in the attic!

This afternoon a steady beating rain and a northeast wind made the dark September day an ideal one for poking behind the old chests and into the cupboards back by the chimney. Betty had been "pretending" some of the exciting parts of the Waverly novels. The gloomy corners, the deep chests, the closets whose contents could scarcely be seen, even the hanging strings of onions all helped in creating an air of mystery and romance.

Now Betty was ready to settle down on the deep seat of the little window that came almost to the floor, and read further in *Redgauntlet*. As she curled up, her hand felt a knob under the window sill. She pulled out a drawer which she had never found before. Inside were some small old calf-bound books and a yellow newspaper. Betty looked at the newspaper. Such a small sheet, and such heavy black type. Then her eye was caught by the curious words of the column headed "Advertisements":

Whoever stole a lot of hides, on the fifth of the present month, is hereby informed that the owner has a sincere desire to be his friend. If poverty tempted him to this false step, the owner will keep the whole transaction secret, and will gladly put him in the way of obtaining money by means more likely to bring him peace of mind.

What an amazing advertisement! Just then Betty heard her grandmother coming upstairs to the attic.

"Grandmother!" cried Betty almost before that lady had reached the top step. "Listen to this," and Betty read her the strange advertisement.

Grandmother finished pulling out from a trunk the quilts that she wanted before she replied. Then she sat down on an old chair and said:

"I haven't thought of that for years. It is an interesting story. Grandfather and I put that advertisement in the paper."

"You did! Please tell me about it," begged Betty.

"Well, grandfather had been working on a quantity of valuable hides, tanning them with especial care. One night he thought he heard a noise coming from the barn, and he went to the kitchen door. But all he saw in the darkness was a man, staggering under a heavy load, entering the yard of the Townsend place. The next morning the hides were gone.

"At that time the tenant house on the Townsend farm was occupied by a wretched family, the father of which was so discouraged that he was drunk a great deal of the time and seemed perfectly worthless. They were really our nearest neighbors, and we used frequently to find their starved old cow in our young corn, tools borrowed and returned broken, and all manner of things done to annoy.

"So of course grandfather's first impulse was to go straight to this man and accuse him of the theft. But, as we talked it over, he suddenly decided on a different course of action. We knew that the wife and children were suffering from actual want, which we had tried in vain to relieve, and it seemed too bad to add this disgrace to their misfortunes. So grandfather determined to try putting this notice in the paper.

"We heard nothing of it for three days after the paper

was out. Then, just after we had put the cat down cellar, and were about to light the candle for bed, we heard a knock at the shed door. It was rainy and cold, just such a night as this will be."

Grandmother unconsciously patted the quilts in her lap.

"I felt certain instantly who it was, and, sure enough, grandfather opened to find our neighbor, hat pulled down over his eyes, hides upon his shoulder. For an instant he did not speak, then he muttered, 'I've brought these back, Mr. Savery. Where shall I put them?'

"'Wait until I can light a lantern, and I will go to the barn with thee,' grandfather answered. 'Then perhaps thou wilt come in and tell me how this happened.'

"While they were out I flew around, down to the vault for a pumpkin pie, boiled the kettle for coffee and got down a cured beef to slice. When they came in, I spoke up: 'Neighbor, I thought perhaps a bite of supper would be good for thee.'

"He was just inside the door, and I remember he wheeled with his back to me so quickly that I thought he was going right out. Instead, he leaned his arm against the door and buried his face in the crook of his elbow, and I declare I was frightened the way his shoulders shook and heaved. Grandfather motioned to me to keep quiet, and in a few minutes, without turning around, the poor fellow said in a choked voice, catching his breath as a child does after hard sobbing:

"'It's the first time I ever stole anything. I don't know what's come over me, with the drink and the quarrels! I never'd thought I'd come to this, but now since I've started down hill everybody gives me a kick—except you. Yet how I hated you for the meals you sent to the wife and children! She's sick—they're starving. I stole the hides, meaning to sell them the first chance I got. Then I read your notice in the paper. What's the use——' his voice was smothered with those awful sobs.

"Grandfather's voice was just as gentle and friendly, without a bit of that soft pity that would have stirred up the man's bitter pride.

"'Tonight begins a new life, my friend,' he said, 'Thou art still young and it is in thy power to make up for lost time. Promise me that thou wilt not touch liquor for a year, and tomorrow I will employ thee at good wages. Thy boy can help earn, too, at least pick up stones in the south pasture. Forget the hides—that was thy first theft, and thy last. Come, eat now, and drink some of Mary's coffee. She will always make it for thee when it will help quiet the craving. Keep up a brave heart, man, for the sake of thy wife and children.'

"With that our guest sat down at the table, though at first he couldn't eat; and I left them, thinking he might feel easier with no woman about. When I returned he had gone, having finished what I had put before him. Grandfather said that he had promised solemnly, God helping him, to lead a different life if grandfather would only stand by him."

"That was a funny way to treat a thief," said Betty thoughtfully, her eyes on the overgrown little path to the Townsend place that could still be distinguished in the dark afternoon. "And did he keep good?"

"Indeed he did!" said grandmother. "He was our right-hand man for years. It seemed that he loved every animal on this farm because it was grandfather's."

"It's no wonder everybody loves grandfather," said Betty. "Let's go downstairs and find him."

WHO IS MY NEIGHBOR?

ERNEST hung over the rickety porch railing, watching the new family move in next door. Aunt Lizzie, working around in the house, remembered to call him every once in a while, because, as he knew already, she did not want him to have anything to do with these new neighbors, but he never had to stay inside very long. Soon Aunt Lizzie's attention would shift to the brass bedstead or the pink lampshade that was being carried up the steps next door, and while she peered through the stiff lace curtain, her nose wrinkled in disapproval, Ernest dodged out again.

He greatly enjoyed seeing people move their possessions. There was continual changing in this shabby Chicago neighborhood, where Ernest's family was the only one left from its better days, thirty years ago; but this new family was different and more important even than the first Jewish family that had come to live in the block. Aunt Lizzie had been terribly worried when she heard about them. She said to Ernest's father, "Joe, you've got to move now, I tell you I can't bring up your boy decent with a Nigger family next door!" But Father had only said in his tired voice, "Find the money, Lizzie. I can't!"

Ernest himself was perfectly happy where he was. He liked the families that moved in; they had a great many small children, who were largely left to take care of themselves and so they had plenty of time to play with Ernest, who had no brothers and sisters. This new family seemed to him especially promising, although he did not tell Aunt Lizzie that he thought so.

There were four brown children who smiled dazzlingly across at Ernest's interested face; not to mention an admirable brown baby who never once cried in its bed improvised from a bureau drawer and a pillow. Excited with the joys of moving, the smaller children bustled about, placing themselves perilously in the path of the movers; but the older boy, whom they hailed as Clifford, was of real use. He carried in chairs and pots and pans, and between times he herded the smallest toddler. Ernest's heart went out to him. He was a big boy, at least ten to Ernest's eight, but, unlike most big boys, he was not at all superior. His wide grin showed a spirit of complete equality.

Later, looking through the back fence palings, Ernest saw Clifford mending a fine packing-box wagon, which ran very well, though only two of its wheels were mates; and which Ernest guessed Clifford had made, as indeed he had. He and his little brothers played new games, shouting with laughter, making up songs as they went along. Most wonderful of all, he had a home-made violin, so-called, cut from a huge gourd that had grown in the South where they used to live, and he could play real tunes on its strings, though it was even harder to keep tuned than most musical instruments. "Some day," he confided in Ernest, "when the boys grow up, Daddy and me are goin' to buy a real violin."

Ernest could not help being friends with these boys, no matter how conscientiously Aunt Lizzie scolded them all. She forbade his going over to the Watsons' yard, and of course they were not allowed in Ernest's yard. She tried to get Ernest's father to speak to the Watsons too, but Father only shut his lips tight and said he had never had trouble with his neighbors and he did not intend to begin now.

As the summer grew hotter Ernest begged to be allowed to go over to the lake. Aunt Lizzie objected at first. The lake was near them, but in order to reach it the boys had to cross a wide stretch of railway tracks that bordered it and scramble through a cindery, weedy waste to the breakwater, a roughly dumped wall of big rocks, held in place with high wooden pilings. Aunt Lizzie could not go with Ernest and she was afraid for him to go alone. "Sam and Abie Cohen will take me," begged Ernest; and Aunt Lizzie agreed doubtfully. "There's some rough boys goes over there," she warned him. "Don't you get mixed up in their fights!"

Ernest set off joyfully to join the good-natured Sam and Abie. "Whyn't you ask Clifford?" he suggested. "He can really swim." "So can I, with water-wings," returned offended Sam, but nevertheless he went on the errand and presently reappeared with a comet's trail of brown followers. Well out of sight of Aunt Lizzie, Ernest added himself to the procession, and presently they found themselves clambering up on the breakwater with the grateful lake breeze in their hot faces.

The rough wall was already crowded. Clifford took one keen, experienced look along it and marshalled his little brothers at·the far end, where some other colored boys had already gathered. Once among them the Watsons took off their shirts and placed Buddy, the youngest, comfortably on them, with instructions to stay there. All of them could swim like ducks, but Clifford helped perfect them in the fine art of standing on their heads in the water, before he swam out to a distance where he would not allow them to follow.

Ernest watched them wistfully from a distance. He had been in the water so seldom that he was timid and dared not venture out of reach of the pilings, where the water was about waist depth. He wished Clifford would come and teach him, but he was beginning to be afraid that he would not. A colored boy who had paused on the breakwater near Ernest to watch the diving had been rudely shoved by two or three newly arrived white boys. "Get

along, Nigger," they shouted, "You don't belong here!"
The colored boy hesitated angrily, but finally went down
with the other colored boys, where he explained indig-
nantly what had happened, while the white boys hooted
at them.

Presently Ernest forgot this incident, which had given
him an unpleasant feeling in his stomach, in the pleasure
of realizing that Clifford was coming his way. "Oh gee,
teach me, won't you?" he begged as Clifford's shining face
appeared from the splash of his last fine stroke. "Suah,"
answered Clifford, "that what I come fo'." He came to his
feet. "Jus' lay down in the wate' with you' chin in my
hand." Ernest obeyed directions fearfully, and in the excitement of his floundering he failed to see a curious little
attacking party coming up the breakwater. Clifford, attracted by a growing disturbance, looked up to see four or
five colored boys, including the boy who had been ordered
away earlier, advancing up the rough stone path, shoving
the white boys out of their way as they came. They met
with no resistance at first. The white boys were too much
astonished at this show of spirit from the colored boys; some
of them were members of tough gangs, who expected every
one else, white or black, to get out of their paths. The
quiet did not last long. The first boy who recovered his
breath seized a sharp fragment of rock and let fly. In less
time than it takes to tell, the air was full of flying stones,
reinforcements had hurried up on both sides, and a serious
battle was on.

Clifford had no desire at all to join the fight. Stones
were splashing around them; he put his left arm up over
his face and towed the surprised Ernest as fast as he could
toward a spot in the breakwater where the pilings were
not driven so closely. Arrived at this point, he stuffed
Ernest's thin body into this crevice and stood in front of

him, protecting him as well as he could from falling stones.

In a lull in the angry shouting above them a wail from farther down the breakwater came to their ears. "Wha's that?" breathed Clifford anxiously. "Sounds like Buddy. He might be gettin' hurt. Ernest, you' a big boy. Couldn't you take care you' self, while I go see 'bout Buddy?"

He turned to work his way down the breakwater, when a voice from overhead yelled, "Fellers, here's one! I got y', Nigger!" With all his strength Clifford shouted, "Don't th'ow! There's a white boy here!" and threw himself again in front of poor Ernest.

If they heard, they did not understand, but, leaning over the pilings to take better aim, one caught sight of Ernest's frightened face, and was the more enraged. "He's got a white boy down there! Kill 'im!" he shrieked, and the cry, "Kill 'im! Kill 'im!" ran through the mob. Stones rained around them. Ernest was not hurt but Clifford was struck several times, once with a jagged bit of rock that cut open his forehead. He swayed where he stood, and in a breathing spell, while his attackers were hunting fresh ammunition, he slid down in the water and disappeared, leaving only a tiny streak of blood.

"Where's he gone, kid?" a boy called to Ernest, peering down for his late target. "I don't know," sobbed Ernest. "He fell down in the water."

"Hey, fellers, the Nigger's drowned," the boy announced with great interest. Like magic the battle subsided. Ernest was hauled up on the breakwater, and as he sat there trembling, he saw to his great amazement that white as well as black were diving, searching for Clifford's body. They found nothing, and at a warning cry of "Cops!" all of them scurried half-dressed for the overhead bridge. Ernest was dragged along in the guilty flight by Sam and Abie, who had emerged from safe hiding-places.

Ernest could not stop crying. He ducked around to the back yard to save explaining his trouble to Aunt Lizzie, and there—he could not believe his ears and yet his eyes told the same story! In the Watson's back yard sat Clifford and his little brothers drying in the sun, while Clifford made the usual daily repairs on the packing-box wagon.

"H-how did you get here?" Ernest managed to ask, and all the brown faces looked up.

"Swum under wate'. Then I got Buddy and we chased home. Buddy was sittin' on the shirts jus' like I told him," said Clifford proudly while Buddy beamed.

"I'm going to tell Aunt Lizzie what you did for me," offered Ernest. It was a brave intention, in its way, but he could see the cut on Clifford's forehead, and he noticed one arm was stiff.

"You think you bette'?" asked Clifford, doubtfully; he watched the kitchen door after Ernest had gone in, with the air of one who must be ready to move rapidly; but nothing happened for a long time and gradually he became absorbed in tuning his gourd violin.

The shadows were long when Ernest finally showed a crestfallen face through the fence. "She wouldn't believe me," he confessed. "She said she knew I'd get in a fight if I went to the lake and so I couldn't go any more this summer. She wouldn't believe a word I told her about you."

"Neve' min'," Clifford comforted him. "She can't help it. Seems as if some white folks was like that. You want play my violin? I'll let you!"

Ernest swallowed hard with shamed pride and conflicting joy. "Clifford," he said solemnly, "I won't ever care if you're colored! I—I wouldn't care even if you was colored green or blue!" And they all laughed in happy understanding.

Marjorie Hill Allee

A RIDE TOWARD WAR PAINT

"BY SUNDOWN we should be within sight of the Indian village," said Caleb Pusey as the six men on horseback descended the rough trail and came out in the glare of the afternoon sun. Below them spread a wide Pennsylvania valley, as yet untouched by a plow, for this was in the early days of the colony, long before the Revolutionary War.

"It lies just beyond yonder line of trees, does it not?" asked a younger man, James West, pointing down the valley.

Caleb nodded gravely. All the men looked extremely serious as in silence they guided their horses among the loose rocks and around fallen trees. Then one man spoke:

"Caleb, who was it brought the word to our settlement of the Indian uprising? You know I was not present last night when the Councillors met."

"It was old Red Wing's squaw. They were always most friendly to the whites. She came into the village late in the afternoon and stopped the first man she met, who happened to be the blacksmith. From his forge the news spread like fire, and I have never seen such panic. It was said five hundred, nay a thousand, Indian warriors were gathering for battle—their faces were painted—their drums were beating—at any moment they would be upon us! Forgotten were the wise counsels of William Penn and the long, unbroken peace with our red brothers. The talk was all of arming and marching against the Indians before they could reach us. Our settlers have never had arms—or needed them. Now they must be procured! The Council was called for immediate action."

"Ah, I wish you had heard Caleb at that meeting!" cried James West with boyish enthusiasm. "In the midst of the argument of the Councillors as to where guns could be procured, Caleb rose and his eyes shone like coals——"

"It was my heart that burned with shame for my people," murmured Caleb.

James continued eagerly, "He cried in a voice that silenced their frantic bickerings, 'I will go to the place where the Indians are said to be gathering, if the Council will appoint five others to go with me unarmed.' The Council protested. They said it would be but a living sacrifice. The six men would be surely murdered. Caleb declared that as long as we were unarmed and unafraid, we were safe, as we always had been."

Caleb took the story up. "James, here, was at my side in an instant. These other good friends expressed their approval and willingness to go. I knew that I could depend on you. So the Council could not well refuse to allow us to depart on our errand, though they had little faith. I do not doubt, myself, that when we talk to the Indian chiefs we can discover the trouble and put matters right."

The others nodded. Still each man realized, in spite of these cheery words, that they were running a grave risk. Indians when once aroused, do not listen to argument. The hearts of the six white men beat faster as at last they came within sight of the tepees of the Indian village.

A few yellow curs barked shrilly and two little brown children playing on the edge of the woods, ran away and peeped at the strangers from behind trees. There was no other sign of life. Most of the wigwams were closed as if deserted. From the peak of one, larger than the rest and near the center of the field, rose a lazy curl of smoke. The men rode to it. An old Indian, evidently the chief, lay on a pile of skins outside the open flaps, peacefully smoking a

carved red-clay pipe. He rose slowly and stood courteously
before the white men. They dismounted, and Caleb of-
ered the Indian his hand, which the old man shook
warmly, inquiring in broken English, "What can an old
chief do for his paleface friends?'

The thought crossed James West's mind that perhaps
this was a trap, perhaps the warriors were all hidden ready
to spring out upon them, or had already departed to attack
the settlement of whites. Almost breathlessly he waited for
the chief's answer when Caleb Pusey asked, carelessly:

"Your tepees seem empty, Chief. Where are your young
men and maidens?"

The Chief waved his hand toward the forest beyond the
valley.

"For three days my men have been hunting deer far
away to the north. The women, old and young, are working in the fields beyond the river. What could my people
do for the strangers?"

The sincerity of the old man's desire to be friendly was
so evident that the white men were embarrassed and
ashamed to have to explain their errand.

"The truth is that a false report reached the ears of the
white settlers, and we were sent to determine whether it
could be true," Caleb began. "An Indian woman told us
that the tribes were rising against us."

The Chief stepped back as though he had been struck,
his eyes blazing with anger.

"It is false!" he cried. "That woman should be burned
to death, for she might have made much mischief! We
have no quarrel with the white men."

THE WATER BARREL

"DAVID, Father and I are leaving one thing for you to attend to this morning," Mother said, as she took her gloves and pocketbook from the drawer and glanced out of the window to see if Father had brought the horse to the door.

"There's Father, waiting for me. Listen, dear? I want you, before you do anything else, to fill the water tank, so that it will last all tomorrow."

"I was going right down to the pasture to help Pete catch the lambs." David's voice sounded a little whining.

"No," replied Mother firmly; "bring up the water first of all, or it may not get done. Father and I will be home by six o'clock. After that one job, you can have fun all the rest of the day. Good-bye."

"Good-bye," David called, as the carriage rattled down the lane.

He walked back into the house and straight through to the kitchen. They were proud of this house—David and his father and mother—for it was very new and had taken a long time to build. Parts of it still were not finished. The well had not been drilled, so that all the water had to be carried from the spring, instead of being brought into the house through pipes. It was David's special work to keep water in a large barrel fastened firmly on a strong platform over the kitchen sink. His mother could then draw it from a spigot connected with the bottom of the barrel.

David climbed up a few steps on the side of the barrel, and, leaning far over the rim, tried to see how much water was left. It was so low that he couldn't even touch the surface with his finger tips. He sighed and got the bucket out from under the sink. He was a strong little boy—almost twelve years old—and he wasn't a bit tired, but it made him sigh to think of all the things he wanted to do that cool, sunshiny morning.

After the first five buckets had been poured into the barrel, with violent splashings, David sat down on the kitchen step to rest. He could see Pete, the hired man, down in the sheep pasture.

"I wonder why it wouldn't do just as well if I finished carrying water this afternoon," he thought. "What's the difference to Mother, so long as I get it done?"

He got up and was starting down the path when he remembered the last time Mother had gone to town. She and Father had been away all Sunday, and he had promised to have the barrel filled for the Monday washing. Well, as it turned out, he had let it go—and Monday morning Mother couldn't do the wash because Father, Pete and David had all gone to haul a load of lumber, and no one was there to carry in water.

David turned back, kicking pebbles impatiently. "Five more buckets, and I'll call it enough," he muttered. One bucket—two buckets—three—four—the sun was getting very hot—five—at last! Again he climbed the steps and leaned over the brim. The surface of the water glimmered more than half-way up the barrel, but still it wasn't nearly full.

David knew that by this time Pete had finished with the lambs and would be mending fence in the south pasture. Blue-berries were thick over there. David felt very hungry. He picked up the bucket and said to himself, "Two more, and then I'm through!" Suddenly it occurred to him that it would be fun to *fill* the old barrel once, really, entirely, full. Always before he had stopped as soon as possible, which meant, of course, that the supply ran out so much the sooner. He ran down to the spring with fresh enthusiasm. One bucket—it slopped over and wet his shoes a little. Two buckets—that time he almost stumbled over the step and spilled it all. Three buckets—it certainly was getting very heavy! Four buckets—Pete called to him, "Come on down here with me, boy," and David only answered shortly, "I'm busy." Five buckets. The water didn't make much noise now when it was poured in. Six buckets—David poured very slowly, looking over the edge as he did so. Close to his face was the black shadow of his own head, and the barrel was full to the brim.

"Whoopee! Pete—sixteen buckets—and it's chuck up full!" yelled David, leaping madly and waving his arms with joy.

An hour later, Pete stopped digging his posthole and stared at the distant house: "David!" he cried excitedly, "look at that smoke. Where's it coming from?"

David mounted to the top rail of the fence and shaded his eyes. "Seems to be out of the cellar window on this side," he answered.

Without another word, Pete ran at top speed across the fields, David after him. The kitchen was thick with smoke, which seemed to be pouring up from the cellar. Pete plunged down the steps, but was back again in an instant, coughing and choking.

"The long piece of hose from the barn—run, boy, run! That wood in the cellar is smouldering!" He staggered to the sink and grabbed up the bucket.

Dragging the hose after him, David panted back again, too breathless to ask questions. He watched Pete screw one end of the hose to the spigot under the water barrel, tie a wet towel over his nose and mouth, and with a muffled "Stay right here unless I call," dive down again into the smoke.

It seemed hours to David that he alternately stood as near as he could to the cellar door, listening to Pete tumbling things around below, and climbed to peer into the tank. The water sank lower and lower. The hissing, as Pete poured it through the hose on the crackling wood, became fainter. Suppose the barrel ran dry before the fire was out! They would have to carry water in the bucket all the way from the spring. It occurred to David that he might be hauling some now, and then he remembered Pete had said, "Stay right here." Perhaps Pete was afraid the smoke might overcome him and he would need help. David did not dare to stir. The crackling had stopped entirely now—only thick rolls of smoke poured up the stairway and out of the door and windows. Silence below. David was scared. Had anything happened to Pete? The smoke was lighter now. He crept on the floor close to the steps and called. He was startled to hear Pete's voice quite close: "I'm comin', boy."

For five minutes Pete lay on the grass outside, breathing very hard. He was so black that David wanted to laugh, but was afraid he would cry instead. After a while Pete rolled over and looked at the boy sitting beside him.

"Close shave, Dave! There for a while I thought the house was gone. All that dry lumber afire! Must have been started by what they call 'spontaneous combustion' in that pile of wet rags the workmen left. Say, boy"—he sat up slowly—"how'd it ever happen that the water barrel was full? All the time I was squirtin' water I kept thinkin', 'If the water'll just hold out, I can save her yet.' But I never s'posed there'd be so much in the barrel. Just enough to kill the last flicker—and a bit less wouldn't have done!"

"I filled it chuck full this morning," David answered.

"Well, let me tell you then—you saved this nice, brand-new house of your pa's from burning to a cinder! Put it there, old chap!" David's hand was swallowed up in Pete's grimy fist, and he grinned proudly.

SAM

ʏʏ

SAM was Timmy's best friend in all the world. That was his name, just Sam for Samuel and nothing more. Timmy had two names. Probably you have three names and if your parents thought you were something extra special, or if there were too many aunts and uncles to please, then you, poor thing, have four names. But as I was saying, some people—people whom the world considers unimportant—have only one name.

Sam's skin was black like coal. It really doesn't make any difference what color a person's skin is, not really. I only mention it for this reason: because his skin was black Sam was a slave. At the time of this story there were many slaves in America. The bigger the man's farm the more slaves he required to do the work. Did everybody think it was all right to own slaves? Well, that's what this story is about. Some did, and some didn't.

Timmy never thought about Sam's being a slave, he only thought of him as the best friend in all the world. Nobody knew Sam's age; he might have been a hundred, you couldn't tell. He was thin all over, hands, face, shoulders, and so thin in the middle that he bent right over just like those willow trees that go up and come back down. You musn't suppose because Sam was so old and thin that he was sickly and lazy. Not a bit. He was first up in the morning, lighting fires, preparing the breakfast, and all day long he worked, quiet and steady. He was never hurried, never excited, never bored with what he was doing. Whatever he did, the most insignificant thing, if he picked up a rope, fastened a gate, stroked a calf, or pulled a carrot, it was done deliberately and you felt comfortable about it. You felt that it was just what he ought to be doing out of all the things in the world to be done.

Wherever Sam was, Timmy was sure to be close by. The old man would talk quietly, showing him how to do everything that was useful under the sun, and when Timmy learned quickly and remembered, then old Sam's black eyes would sparkle and he would pat Timmy gently with his long stiff hand. Timmy never questioned where Sam came from, he just accepted him like his home, like the earth and the sky—things always near, always there making him secure and happy.

Timmy was a member of a Quaker meeting, and in those days that meant being a part of a great big family that met together twice a week in the meeting house to worship God. On the first day of the week farm chores were done as early as possible and then down the road the whole family would walk, almost a mile to the meeting house. Timmy's mother and father would walk together and behind them came Timmy and Sam, hand in hand. Timmy's mother and father were called "elders" and this meant that with certain other Friends they would sit in front, facing the meeting. So Tim and Sam would sit on a bench by the door.

As you may guess, Tim sometimes grew a little weary sitting there an hour-and-a-half or two hours at a time, but still he loved going to meeting; it was the center of the world to him. As silence spread over the meeting it seemed like a great tent drawn close around all who waited together expectantly. He would look up to the elders sitting in front and study each face he knew so well. Side by side were Joshua Andrews aged 101, Harrison Smith aged 99, Morton Price aged 98 and Jacob Coale aged 102—all in all, he had heard his father say, a total of 400 years! Then he would spend a long time thinking about what the world was like four hundred years ago—something he and Sam had talked about at great length. It might be a long time before anyone would speak in meeting and Tim would lay his tired head over on Sam's lap—not to go to sleep, oh no, just to look out the window and imagine that he was a bird flying high above all the people; but before long his eyes would close and he *would* be sound asleep and know nothing more till he felt Sam shaking his hand and he knew that meeting was over.

Frequently there would come visiting ministers and then Tim would try extra hard to stay awake to see what this strange new person might be like.

One day there came a traveling minister whose name was Isaac Jackson, and he was "traveling with a concern". In those days every Quaker boy or girl knew what that meant: Let us suppose that it is a nice summer day and you want to go swimming and so, asking permission from your mother, you start walking with your friends to the river. You would be traveling, but hardly with a "concern"; you wanted to go, it was good to go, but you really didn't have to. But now let us suppose that when you are almost to the river you remember that your mother said that you were to stop on the way and deliver a message to Mrs. Jones. You say to yourself, "It doesn't make any difference, I can deliver it some other time, I can't leave my friends now." But something inside you just won't let you be comfortable, because you had promised to deliver the message on the way. So you turn around and start walking back to Mrs. Jones's house—*then* you would be traveling with a concern. You knew you wouldn't feel right inside unless you obeyed and so you did.

That's the way it was with Issac Jackson. He had a concern. Something inside him just wouldn't be still until he obeyed. What was this concern? It was to travel up and down the land, stopping at every Quaker community and inquiring how many families there held slaves. Into those households he would go, very quietly asking the Friends if they were untroubled in their minds about holding slaves. And if he found them of a tender spirit—that was the expression they used then—he would urge them to go ahead with what they knew to be right.

The morning that Isaac Jackson visited Timmy's meeting, no sleepy head dropped down on Sam's lap; Timmy wanted to hear what this tall stranger might sound like. It was a long time before he rose to speak, but Tim waited without moving a muscle, wondering whether he would have a big booming voice, since he was such a big man. What a surprise! It was a soft musical voice, like the singing of the wind in the pine trees outside the meeting house. It was a voice that came like the wind from nowhere and went singing on in one's mind when the talking had ended. Isaac Jackson started speaking as though he were suddenly, quietly, letting others in on an inward conversation, or better still, as if it were a song that had been singing within him for a long time. It was an ancient song, begun centuries ago by an oppressed, despised people, a people in slavery. Then the song modulated, that is his voice came nearer and he spoke of things of the present day, of that slavery which binds the very man who would try to bind his brother. "Free men," he said, "are those who fear to sit in the seat of judgment over another's life, who quake lest they walk in the path of oppression, and who disdain those vanities which make great the burden of the poor. Many prosperous Christians now living shall stand aside at the gate of the Kingdom of Heaven while others who are now in chains shall go in before them. Christ came to make men free spirits, but we deny Him, yea more, we scoff at Him, we spit upon Him when we presume to hold another's life within our hands."

These were fearful words to break the Quaker silence. Timmy didn't understand their full meaning, as perhaps you don't either, but he did feel that some strange power was there in the meeting house. It was as if a flash of lightning had struck in their midst and all were fearful to move even their smallest finger lest they find themselves to be the stricken one. He didn't understand all the minister's words, but he knew it was now a different world from the happy one he had come to meeting in that morning. He wanted all during the rest of meeting, and on the way home, to look at Sam. But for the first time in his life he was afraid to. He wanted to turn and look into Sam's big dark eyes and say, "Sam, you are free, aren't you?" and then to hear Sam reply, "Little boy, what are you talkin' about! Of course I am free. There you go with your strange imaginin's. Wouldn't I have told you if I wasn't free as that bird on the fence post over there?"

Timmy tried on the way home to bring the question to his lips, but it just wouldn't come. Perhaps Sam would turn his question off as he sometimes did and say, "Now little boy, it's all accordin' to how you interp'et this thing freedom." Or then again he might say the awful thing, "Little boy, that's the way it is, you'll learn, some is born to be slaves and some is not."

What difference did it make to Timmy, you ask, whether Sam was a slave or not? An awful lot. Sam was his best friend in all the world! And if Sam wasn't as free, not really as free as he was to go over and paddle in Miller's pond, well then, Timmy thought, he might just as well go out to the hay stack, bury himself in the middle of it, and stay there forever and ever. Repeatedly in the next two days, which were the saddest in his young life, he walked round and round the hay stack with this in mind. He kept out of the way of Sam and his mother and father those two days. The second evening his mother decided he was ill so she gave him some herb tea and put him to bed early.

At the time that Timmy was being put to bed, Isaac Jackson, the traveling Friend, was sitting comfortably in the home of Josiah Miller. He was tired, but happy in the tiredness that comes at the end of a long task faithfully done. He had been gone from home almost five months and tomorrow he would turn homeward with a free mind, his concern carried out. He had visited the owners of eleven hundred slaves! Now he might rest awhile. But as he sank back in a chair by the fire he found his mind's eye resting on the face of old Sam, just as in the meeting two days before. Was this slave number 1101? Was this still another visit to be made? Josiah Miller had told him *that* was one visit he needn't be concerned for; Sam was so old, he was perfectly cared for, perfectly happy. If ever a case might be left to take care of itself this was it. Isaac Jackson tried to put his mind on other things. It was no use, there was that sad face with those dark eyes before him, and he knew what he had to do. So he expressed his uneasiness and Harry Miller, the young son of the host, eagerly offered to go with him and show the way in the dark.

The sound of horses and the cheery voice of Harry Miller woke Timmy from a light sleep and peering out the window he saw his young neighbor friend and Isaac Jackson tying their horses. Timmy's heart pounded hard as he gathered up his nightgown and slipped quietly down the stairs, seating himself on the bottom step where he could peek through a little crack in the door.

Isaac Jackson was telling how uneasy he felt about their old slave; Timmy couldn't see the minister but he could hear his kindly, urgent voice.

"We have, of course, thought of it many times," Timmy's father replied, "but it wouldn't make any difference in the old man's life now. He has always lived in our family and always will. What difference can it make to him as long as he is well cared for?"

"I am not sure," came the slow reply, "just what difference it would make, but I know that is the way that all the world is coming to reason it, and that's the cause for all our sorrow. Thou and I go by the name of Christian. If we, like the world's people go about deciding the issue of other men's lives, if we reason from humanly conceived consequences rather than from divine principle, then we had best cast aside that great name. Come now, I am not saying what thou shouldst do, I am only asking if we should do what we know to be good without questioning the result."

Timmy's father agreed that this was true and Isaac Jackson immediately produced a manumission paper, a stock of which he must have carried with him. When this was signed, the minister asked that Sam be brought in. Sam seated himself on his accustomed stool by the fire; his form was nearly double, his thin hands were propped on his knees, his white head was thrust forward, and his keen, restless, inquiring eyes glanced alternately toward the stranger and toward his master. The visiting Friend remained silent. At last the master spoke, in tones so strange and broken, that Timmy hardly knew it for his father's voice. He told of the paper that had just been signed, that Sam was no longer a slave, and that his master acknowledged his past services entitled him to a maintenance so long as he lived.

The old man listened in almost breathless wonder, his head slowly sinking on his breast. After a short pause, he clasped his hands, then spreading them high over his hoary head, slowly and reverently exclaimed, "Oh, Goody Gody, oh!"—bringing his hands again down upon his knees. Then raising them as before, he twice repeated the solemn exclamation, and with streaming eyes and a voice almost too much choked for utterance, he continued, "I thought I should die a slave, and now I shall die a free man!"

It is hard to say what might have happened after that, if Timmy hadn't been sitting listening by the door, but I can tell you what did happen. A little boy's nightgown got tangled up, and losing his balance, Timmy fell against the door which flew open and out he rolled right in front of the fireplace, just like a little bear rolling out of its cave. Nobody laughed. Nobody had time. Before anybody could say a word old Sam picked him up in his arms, just as if he had been a bag of chicken feathers.

"Little boy," he said, "it's time you was in bed dreamin' about the angels."

"I would rather be with you than with the angels," said Timmy as the old man tucked him in.

"Angels is good for the night time and you can be with me tomorrow."

"Oh good," whispered Timmy. "Can we go over to Miller's pond and catch some perch?"

"After chores are over we'll ask your father."

"But you are free, Sam, you don't have to ask anybody."

"How about you, little boy, is you so free you don't have to ask anybody about anything—nobody is that free, I guess. Somehow everybody is connected up to somebody."

"Yes," said Timmy dreamily, "I like that," and almost immediately he fell fast asleep.

Gilbert Kilpack

THE PEACEFUL SOLDIERS

RAMASWAMI was tired! All day long he had been working in the fields under the blazing sun of South India. He was hungry, too, but he was used to that. Except at the time of a wedding or some other celebration when he could eat until he was quite filled, he never had enough to eat. Today he had brought from home a little rice gruel in an earthenware vessel. That was all he had eaten all day. His wages of sixteen cents a day never seemed to buy enough food for the family. Sometimes there were days when there was no work. To be sure his wife could often earn eight cents a day, and the children as much as four cents, but the combined wages were not enough to keep them from being hungry all the time. It was now six o'clock. Soon he would be eating the one regular meal of the day. Then he could rest till morning. Wearily he shouldered the short handled hoe with which he had been working, balanced his red earthen gruel pot on his head, and started for home with his companions.

Between him and home lay a walk of nearly two miles. He must skirt the town of Vykom, past the cactus hedges, walking always with his eyes on the ground lest he step on a thorn, or on one of the many poisonous snakes that live in the cactus. It wasn't a pleasant walk.

According to the census report Ramaswami lived in the town of Vykom. Actually he lived just outside the town in what was called the "Cheri," the outcaste quarters, the home of the Untouchables. Ramaswami was by birth an "Untouchable." There was nothing he could ever do about it. He must not go near people of higher castes; he must not walk down the streets where they lived; he must always live in the "Cheri."

In the center of the town of Vykom stands a large Hindu temple. On all sides of the temple are the homes of the Brahmans, the highest of all castes, the priests of the Hindu temple. The main road to the town goes by the Cheri where Ramaswami lived, straight to the big temple. There it divides to go around the high red and white striped walls of the temple past the houses of the Brahmans. Then it comes together again, and goes on out through the town by the fields where Ramaswami and his friends worked. It was a much shorter walk than the path past the cactus hedges, only about half the distance.

Tonight as Ramaswami and his companions approached the place where the rough path through the cactus branched off from the main road, they paused a moment to look longingly at the broad smooth road that led to the temple. It was a much pleasanter walk, and a mile shorter. Not one man in the group had ever walked past the Brahmans' houses. Ramaswami had never walked past the temple. His father had never walked past the temple. His grandfather, his great-grandfather, his great-great-grandfather, all his ancestors since the beginning of the world had used the rough thorny path around the town. If they had passed through the Brahmans' street they would have made the street impure: so the Brahmans believed, and so the Untouchables believed. Ramaswami knew that if he tried to walk down that street he would be badly beaten up by the Brahmans. Walking an extra mile was easier than taking a beating, so he turned off onto the narrow thorny path.

As he came near the group of mud huts where he lived, Ramaswami noticed a crowd gathered under the shady tamarind tree. Someone was talking to the people. Ramaswami pushed past the women and children on the edge of the crowd, elbowed his way through the men until he could see the speaker. He was a young Indian Christian by the name of George Joseph. His dress of coarse white homespun cloth was neat and clean. On his head he wore the small white cap that proclaimed him a follower of Gandhi. His speech showed that he was a man of education. He was a lawyer. Just now he was neglecting his profession to help these poor outcaste people. He had been in the village before. As Ramaswami approached, making a low salaam, Joseph turned to speak with him, and enquire about his work.

"I'm tired tonight," said Ramaswami, "and it is a long way around the village."

"What!" exclaimed Joseph. "Do you mean to tell me that you do not use the road through the town?"

"Oh, no, that is not allowed," Ramaswami replied hopelessly.

"But it is a public highway. You have as much right as anyone to walk on it. You outcaste people must stand up for your rights! Otherwise you can never improve your condition. Fight for your rights if need be!" urged Joseph.

"Fight indeed!" Ramaswami and his friends were plainly disgusted. "How can we, who never have enough to eat, and who are always weak and sickly, fight against the well-fed Brahmans, who would call in the police to help them? No—you talk like a crazy man."

Joseph showed no anger at this last insult. "I am a follower of Mahatma Gandhi," he said quietly. "Gandhi believes that Jesus really meant what He told men. He says that the sword of the spirit is stronger than the sword of steel; that soul force is greater than physical force. Our fight must be a peaceful fight. There must be no bloodshed. Such a fight requires braver men than does a battle

with guns. You must be strong enough to love your enemies. If they strike you, you must not strike back. If they
call you names, you must not answer in anger; you must
speak words of love. You must really love them in your
hearts. A peaceful fight is very hard, but we are sure to
win!"

The Untouchables listened in open-mouthed wonder.
Had the hot sun affected the head of their friend? They
began to mutter amongst themselves that no one could fight
as George Joseph urged them to.

Joseph talked on. Ramaswami and the others listened
in spite of themselves, until at last they began to understand a little.

"Tomorrow," said Joseph, "I will go with several of you.
We shall walk in the street past the temple."

Many were afraid to go, but at last several said that they
were willing to begin the battle. The next morning they
started out towards the temple. As they neared the Brahman street, a crowd of angry Brahmans rushed out at them
with long sticks. Shouting, "Out of the way you dirty
dogs! Get along you sons of donkeys!" they beat the outcaste men, and chased them back to the Cheri. They then
returned to their own homes well pleased with themselves
for having driven away the impure outcastes.

Meanwhile the Untouchables were making ready for
the next battle. This one had not been easy. It was hard
not to feel hatred towards the men who had beaten them.
It had been hard not to strike back. They did not know
what a long hard fight was ahead of them, but they did
know that they must go on. George Joseph talked to them
about love. He told them of Gandhi. He read to them
from the Bible of how love is the greater force.

The next morning a larger band of peaceful soldiers
was ready to start for the battlefield.

The Brahmans saw them coming from a distance. They had worn themselves out the day before by hitting the Untouchables so hard, and by allowing themselves to get so angry. They did not feel as if they could strike so hard today, so they called in the State police. The police, looking very fine in their khaki uniforms with red turbans, roughly grabbed the outcastes, and hurried them off to jail. There they were locked up. It looked like a losing fight.

News travels fast in India. How, no white man exactly knows. The third day into Vykom came pouring a crowd of men who believed in fighting with love instead of guns. Most of these men were from high castes, but they were men who believed that the Untouchables had the same rights as high caste men. A group of them took some of Ramaswami's friends to the Brahman street. The police arrested them. So the battle raged, day after day, until it sounded like the story of the locusts carrying away the grains of corn. There came another group of peaceful soldiers with Untouchables, and the police arrested them. Then there came another group of peaceful soldiers with Untouchables, and the police arrested them.

At last the jails were full. It was costing the State money to feed in jail these men, who would not strike back, but who would not give up. The order came to make no more arrests, but for the police to stand in a row across the road to prevent the Untouchables from passing. When another regiment of peaceful soldiers came, the police stood in their way. These men stopped before the police with their hands clasped as if in prayer. Hour after hour they stood in the blazing sun. When they could stand no longer another regiment took their place. Then a third regiment replaced the second. Thus they kept standing in turns day after day. They never spoke an angry word. They tried to keep their hearts filled with love. It was very hard to stand in the hot sun hour after hour. It was harder to keep on loving their enemies. But the hardest time was yet to come.

The war began in the dry season when it is very hot, but never rains. Just as after fall comes winter in America, so in India after the dry season comes the rainy season. It rains every day for about two months. It had been hard to stand in the sun. It was harder to stand in the rain. The police had raincoats supplied by the State. The peaceful soldiers had only one thin cotton homespun garment. Each regiment was soaking wet before it was replaced. Many of them had no change of dry clothes. They tried to dry out their wet clothing around a little charcoal fire. Many caught cold. Many became sick. After it had rained for days the banks of one of the reservoirs broke. Down the street poured a torrent of water. The police were given boats in which to sit. The Untouchables had none. Higher and higher rose the water till it reached the waists of the soldiers.

"Now they will surely give up," thought the Brahmans. To their surprise the Untouchables led by George Joseph stood patiently in the water before the police boats. They did not complain. They only clasped their hands as if in prayer, and waited. "Will they stay there until the water rises over their heads?" asked the Brahmans. "How long must we keep police sitting in boats?" asked the State, "and after all since these Untouchables are citizens why shouldn't they use a public road?" The Brahmans were thinking: "All these months the outcastes have acted like gentlemen. They have not been afraid to suffer. They have not complained. They have not struck back. They have not even called us names. Why shouldn't we allow them to walk past our houses?"

So after months of suffering the victory of Love over Hate was won.

Ramaswami was tired! All day long he had been working in the fields under the blazing sun of South India. Also he was a bit rheumatic from having stood in the water during the peaceful fight, but he was not discouraged. He shouldered his short-handled hoe, balanced his red earthen gruel pot on his head, and started proudly for home. There were two ways that led to the little mud hut where he lived on the other side of Vykom: one was a narrow thorny path around the edge of the town; the other was the broad highway past the high-walled temple. When he and his friends reached the place where the narrow path branched off, they did not even look in that direction. Straight ahead they walked right down the Brahman street. No one chased them away. No one harmed them. They were citizens on a public road. They had a right to live. They had proven that they were brave soldiers who could win a battle without striking a single blow.

Ruth Parker White

THE OLD LADY OF PURCHASE
IIIIIIIIIIIIIIIIIIIIIIIIIIIIIIIIIIIIIIIIIIII

THE lights in the windows of the white houses along the main street of Purchase, New York, were usually out by nine o'clock, just as they had been for all the years since Friends first settled there in 1695.

One stormy October night, however, the window panes at the kitchen end of one little house, though streaked with rain, still glowed cheerfully long after the rest were dark. Here lived an old lady, Sarah Haines, quite alone except for a huge gray cat and a tiny yellow canary. Each evening it was Sarah's custom to put a cover over Dicky's cage to shield him from the lamplight, and to settle herself into the rocking chair beside the cosy wood-stove, Malty purring on the rug. She devoted this time, after all Purchase was asleep, to reading a few chapters of the Bible. During the day she was liable to be interrupted, because every one in the village knew her and loved to stop for a chat.

It was not until ten that she closed her book. She was taking off her spectacles when a heavy thump sounded at the door, as though some one had thrown his weight against it. Malty stopped purring and his eyes grew very large. Sarah laid her spectacles on the Bible and rose briskly, but before she could reach the door the thump came again. She turned the knob, and a man staggered into the room. She caught at his arm, her face all wrinkled with concern.

"Dear me, dear me! Poor man! What ails thee? Such a night to be out—and thy clothes are soaking!"

The wind through the crack blew the flame of the lamp into smoke, and Sarah hastened with some difficulty to push the door shut. The man glanced around the room, but he did not speak. The old lady went on:

"Take thy coat right off and hang it over the chairback by the stove. Here is dry kindling—I will have a blaze in a moment. The oven is already warm." She drew up her own rocker and opened the oven door invitingly. "Put thy feet in there. Dear me, poor man! Thee has walked some distance?"

The man opened his lips for the first time. "Ten miles," he muttered.

"Ten miles—and in this storm! May I not dry thy coat?" The man shook his head. "Not much under it," he replied.

She thought for a moment. "Would thee mind slipping on a coat of my dear husband's that I keep always hanging in the hall closet, though he has not been with me for fifteen years? If thee will just step in here and change." She darted through the doorway and a light flickered in the hall.

The instant she was gone the man sprang to the corner cupboard, his eyes on the silver tea set that shone behind the glass doors. He hesitated, his hand on the knob, when the gentle voice spoke from the doorway.

"Do excuse me, my friend. In my haste to get thee dry clothing I forgot entirely that thee may be suffering more keenly from hunger. I do not keep the food in that cupboard, but while thee is there, will thee please hand down a willow plate from the second shelf, and knife and fork from the box just below. Would thee care for bacon and eggs? They are in the shed."

When Sarah bustled back again she found the man seated at the table near the stove, plate, knife and fork before him. His face was turned away from her and he made no remark while she set a sizzling platter of bacon, with two fried eggs, before him, and asked anxiously, "Did thee change thy coat for my husband's? The coffee is slow in boiling, but will soon be ready. Thee would enjoy a taste of my fresh quince jelly, I expect. I will get it from the cellar."

When she was half way down the cellar stairs, the man said, as though to himself, "No, I can't wear your husband's coat. He was a good man."

He ate, and did not turn again to look at the silver tea set. When the meal was over, Sarah pointed to the sofa with its blue coverlid, which stood in the corner.

"It is late to go out into the storm again tonight. Thee is welcome to sleep here and take breakfast before thee leaves."

Next morning the man did not waken until Sarah shook him by the arm, saying, "The mush is ready." He asked at the breakfast table if the farmers of Purchase needed extra help. Sarah advised him to speak with her brother about getting work on his farm.

As the man left the kitchen, he turned and said, "I knew you lived alone, and I came last night to steal your silver things. But something about you made me change my mind."

The old lady smiled. "No, it was Jesus Christ who changed thy mind."

"Well, maybe so, but He was certainly speaking through you," answered the man.

Anna D. White

THE CHISELED FACE

OLD François sat in the autumn sunshine by the door of his stone cottage. He lived on the very edge of a once happy French village. It was early afternoon, and as the German patrol had passed on its round, and would not return for several hours, François felt a sense of freedom. Into the rough basket by his side he threw handfuls of shreds, made from an old garment, to be used in place of string for tying up his cauliflower plants, on the morrow. A neighbor passed, merely nodded, and went on.

"How strange things are," she said to herself. "No joke with François! Whoever would have believed it four years ago! The poor old stone-carver must have found it hard to work in the fields. How sad he looks, and thin, he that was always so fat, with a merry twinkle in his eye, too." She smiled as she thought of François dropping into her cottage to sing a new snatch of song—through his nose—his cap on the side of his head. Yes, François had always lent the comic element to the village group.

"Well, they can't stay forever," he had said of the Germans, just as the housewife said, "Ah, the flies will go when frost comes."

But the prospect was that the Germans would stay forever. That very morning his daughter, because she was ill, had been sent away with some others back to a part of France that the Germans had not invaded. Now he was left alone to care for her little Julie. He was troubled, because he was so old that he might be sent away very soon, too, and in the meantime he had to spend long hours in the fields.

"Food, food," sighed François, "it is ever food!" Suddenly he thought of Julie. He was not looking after the little one. He put the remaining shreds in his basket, rose, and crept noiselessly around to the north corner of the cottage. "Perhaps she is playing on the stones," he said. Yes, there she was, poor little Julie! quiet as a mouse, hugging an old rag doll-baby and—thinking.

Tears filled old François' eyes as he hesitated a moment, to watch the deserted child. "Ah, why would they not send her with her mother?" François sighed, turned and entered the cottage. He had much to do in a few hours, for his mind was made up to one thing, at least; to-morrow he would take little Julie to the school of the Good Sisters in the next village; then, if the dear God granted his prayer, he would finish cutting the stone face before anything more happened.

He went to the clothes-press, hoping that Julie's things were ready. Yes, there they lay, in a small pile, clean and neat. He got a little basket and laid each garment in tenderly. "Poor baby! poor Julie! with no father or mother at home, not even a grandmother to love her!" "Oh, well, they can't stay forever."

He closed the basket, looked at the clock, and decided that he could go to the cathedral for a little work on the stone face.

How well he remembered the day before the Great War, when he had asked permission of the foreman to do the carving in the gable. "No, no," the man had replied, "it is too high from the ground, Grandfather, you might lose your head and fall."

"But," François had persisted, "I am not so old, and see how stout I am. My head is yet very good, monsieur."

The foreman had laughed. "Very well," he said, and with that François began what he meant to be his greatest work of devotion and praise to God.

"But see," said François, suddenly returning from his reverie, "am I losing my head, to stand gaping at the clock, and only two hours before the patrol returns!"

Hastily calling Julie and taking her little hand in his big one, he left the cottage and went down the hill to the cathedral.

The air was so fresh and the sky so blue that François felt gayer than usual. He would leave the child to play where he could watch her. Then, too, he would try today the new way of going up his stone ladder.

Only the walls of the church were erected, and with much pains, François had cut stones away to make a sort of stairway for himself to a window in the west wall, through which he might reach the upper scaffolding. These footholds were not noticeable, and he hoped that in secret he could continue his carving. Julie dropped down on the ground very languidly with her doll in her arms, and François, making sure that no one was about, slipped quickly inside the church, and began the ascent. He dared not be seen or his plan might fail. Ah, but it dare not fail. François felt that he had promised God to complete the stone face.

Up, up the improvised steps he went. He got on quite well, by grasping the wall firmly. Reaching the top scaffold, he took from his pocket the bit of bread which he hid each day, placed it in a hole in the wall, and closed the opening with a stone to keep it from the birds. Then he worked half an hour, climbed down, and, glad to find that he had been unobserved, took Julie quietly home again.

The next afternoon François put Julie in a small pushcart, with the basket of clothes, and established her at the Sisters' school. As he left, he turned to the picture of the Virgin on the wall, saying, "Holy Mother, thou wilt bless and care for little Julie while she is away from her own!"

And François returned to his cauliflowers and to his secret carving.

Six days later the German officer gave François his order for repatriation.

Now—it had come—the day! After the officer left, François remained standing with the paper in his hand. He felt stunned, but with the numbness was a sense of exhilaration. He had permission to leave the village. His mind reached out into the days ahead of him, his body stood motionless. He was making a great decision. Yes, he would risk it; it was his only chance to finish his work.

That afternoon François worked among his cauliflowers as usual. He tied them up carefully and put all his tools away. Then he went into the cottage, got out some food, hidden in a hole in the floor, and tied it in a red handkerchief. Next he said a short prayer, and reverently unhooking the wooden picture of the Virgin from the wall, wrapped it in another handkerchief and put it inside of his jacket where it would be safe.

These few preparations made, François occupied himself as usual until an hour after the patrol had passed. Then he stole quietly out of the cottage and across the fields to the cathedral.

Before going inside the wall, François sat down under a tree to listen. Not a sound reached his ears except the distant booming from the battle front. All was safe. He rose and entered the church to begin his perilous climb up the stairway in the twilight. He prayed as he groped for each step. When he reached the window, he rested, then, creeping through it, he got out on the upper scaffolding of the west wall. Now he could walk steadily up to the platform on which he worked.

"Dear Lord," he prayed, as he sank down exhausted at the top, "this is to be my sanctuary for many days. Wilt thou grant that this service may be finished before my body grows too feeble to work."

After this night, François began a new life. He awoke when the day dawned, worked while it was safe, then rested, and worked again at times when the sound of his mallet would be unnoticed. He ate as little as possible, and drank little, though rainy days allowed him to catch water and refill his bottles. For two weeks François lived thus. The scanty food and the cold autumn weather told on his strength, but still he toiled on, trying to complete the pictured face of his Lord.

Finally a morning came when his arms were too weak to hold his tools. "Ah, well," said François, "I have all but finished the work. I will eat and drink more today, and perhaps the morning will bring more strength." In the afternoon, he dragged himself up with difficulty, and grasping the wall, got out his crust of bread, but sank back too exhausted to eat it.

The next day, and the next, François lay on his platform unable to rise to his work. The birds chirped, "Rouse up, François, the sun shines!" The fleecy white clouds threw shadows on his body. "Wake! François, wake! The day is fine!" they seemed to call, but the old mason heard nothing. And the beautiful face of the Christ looked down on François' quiet body as though it said, "Thou hast loved me, François, I say to thee, arise!" So he lay.

Then a morning dawned clear and mild, when, suddenly, bells began to ring and whistles to blow; people shouted and laughed. The air seemed full of gladness. "Peace! Peace!" rang the bells. "Peace on earth! Peace! Peace!"

François opened his eyes. Joy filled his soul. Suddenly a voice reached his ears, "Father! Father!" It was his own son bending over him. "Rouse, Father! Listen! It is I,

Jules, your son!" But François only smiled. "I found your chisel below, and so I searched for you," Jules continued; "oh, the Christ!" and little Julie's father gazed with awe upon the stone face. "Thou Son of God," he murmured, "thou hast brought us peace. We thank thee."

Tenderly Jules lifted the shrunken body of the old man and bore him home.

François smiled at everyone but never spoke again, and before the family were reunited, he slept the long sleep in the shadow of the cathedral. But the chiseled face of the smiling Christ shines still upon all the village, bearing witness to the devotion of the old man who carved it there, and who cut the words beneath: "I am the way, follow thou Me."

A MYSTERY TO EVERYONE

In the spring of 1947 the village of Lucimia in Poland was still a bedraggled mixture of blackened ruins, patched-up, makeshift, thatched-roofed shanties and underground hovels made from wartime dugouts or peace-time potato cellars.

It was in a dugout, a six by twelve foot hole in the ground, covered with a V-shaped collection of boards and branches and dirt, that Widow Budniak and her four children lived. There was a straw-covered cot, a stool and a smoky stove and that was home!

No wonder Lucimia was chosen as the location for the first international voluntary work-camp in Poland. And no wonder the village folk all agreed that Widow Budniak should be the first to receive a new home through the help of the Work Campers.

Still, it was a great mystery to everybody . . .

One day a big truck had brought a heavy load of tents and camping supplies and deposited them on the Vistula river bank. The second day the truck came again, crowded with young people who rapidly erected five big tents, set up a stove, hammered together a table and benches and generally made themselves at home under the willow trees by the river. And the third day these young people invited every one in the village to visit the camp and find out what it was all about.

"Here we are, twenty-five volunteer workers, Polish, Danish, English, American, ready to work. What can we do to help you most? We are ready to work without pay, ready to help in any way we can."

"Help me build my house!"

"Help ME build MY house!"

"Build us a school for our children."

"Help us build our homes!"

At first it was bedlam, everybody shouting at once, each one arguing with his neighbor. Finally one man was able to make everybody else be quiet.

"Listen," he said, "first we must find out who you are and why you came and whether you really mean that you are ready to work *without pay!* Nobody does that around here!"

"It's true however," one of the Polish work-campers volunteered. "We Polish students didn't believe it either at first when that man over there invited us to come and promised that the English and American Quakers would pay for all the cost of our food and travel if we'd only come and work. Shall I ask him to tell you why?"

Everybody agreed, so the American leader stepped out and, through an interpreter, briefly explained.

"Many Americans—" he said, "many Polish Americans, many Catholic Americans, many Protestant Americans, many kinds of Americans, as well as many kinds of Englishmen, want peace and friendship, just as Polish people do, just as people all over the world want peace. Many of these Americans and English who have not suffered much from the war, have given money to help those who have suffered terribly from the war. We think the best way to help people is to help them help themselves. We found these Polish students eager to help when we gave them the chance, so here we are. Three more Swiss work-campers and a Finn are coming soon. We have found that the School Inspector says we can bring an old military barrack and erect it for a school if you want it. Several of our girls would like to teach your children in the afternoons if you'd like, even before the school is built. And we have two student doctors who can open a clinic. We're here to help but it is up to you to decide just how we can best help you help yourselves."

It didn't take long for the village folk to decide. Of course they wanted the school—their children had had no schooling at all during the entire seven war years. Of course they wanted the outdoor school started immediately. Of course they wanted the medical clinic—the nearest doctor was twenty miles away! It didn't take more than an hour for the villagers to decide—not without some argument to be sure—which six families most needed help in building their new homes.

The work started the next day so enthusiastically that the discouraged villagers could hardly believe their eyes. Trenches were filled in and the ruins of an old house were cleared away from the site selected for the school. Cement blocks were brought for the foundation, and toward evening, the first sections of the old military barracks arrived. By the end of the week the foundations were completed and erection of the barrack had begun. Each afternoon almost one hundred and fifty children were coming to the Vistula river bank to learn their ABC's though they had no textbooks, paper or pencils. In addition, and with the help of village neighbors, ground was broken for Widow Budniak's new house! Each morning there was a long line-up of peasants waiting patiently for their turn to be treated by the student doctors.

It was not surprising that word of this work-camp spread far and wide.

Just at sunset on the eleventh day a strange truck appeared, jouncing along the rough road beside the dike from the village to the camp beside the river. As it came to a stop at the camp it was seen to be filled with men in uniform. Six soldiers armed with repeating rifles jumped off first! Hastily the American camp leader stepped forward to greet the visitors, but rather gruffly the stocky hard-faced officer in charge strode past and up on the highest part of the bank where he could survey the entire camp! Then the Polish campers stepped forward to answer the barrage of questions:

"What are you doing here?"

"Who are these foreigners running this camp?"

"Who gave them permission?"

"Why did they come?"

"Are they Communists?"

"What are they teaching you?"

Gradually the quiet enthusiasm of the Polish campers made a favorable impression upon the Governor, for this is what the officer proved to be, the Governor or Wojewoda of the entire Kielce province of Poland. He had heard rumors about these foreigners from lands considered not too friendly to his own and he had come to find out for himself. After half an hour of cross-examination and at least partially satisfied with the answers of the work-campers, the Wojewoda turned to the large circle of peasants who had come trooping out from the village to see the excitement. When he asked them what they thought of these foreigners, the answer was unanimous—these foreigners were *all right!*

Finally convinced, the Governor turned back to the American leader. "I have been surprised," he said, "to find everyone here enthusiastic and grateful for your work. Not all foreigners here have been so welcome! We cannot easily forget those who have destroyed our homes and murdered our fathers. But you have come to help, I am convinced of that, and I would be glad if there is some way in which I can help you."

A Polish work-camper was quick to respond. "Indeed

you can help!" she said. "Each day we have one hundred fifty children in our school right here under these willow trees. Could you not send us some beginners' textbooks and other school supplies?"

"Of course I can," the Governor agreed, and then he and his truck-load of soldiers disappeared into the night.

Three weeks later, the Wojewoda returned, bringing with him a big box of books and paper and pencils and crayons, just as he had promised. What is more, he brought with him a big wall map of Poland, the first map of their own country that most of the village children had ever seen.

David S. Richie

OUR WORD IS OUR KEEPER

THOMAS ELLWOOD was sitting in the growing darkness of Newgate Prison, wondering whether the daylight was really gone and if it was time for him to get out the hammock in which he slept and prepare for bed.

"It is hard to know," he said to the man nearest to him, "whether it is more uncomfortable at night or in the daytime."

It was no wonder that he spoke so, for an English prison in 1662 was a very dreadful place. The floors were damp and dirty, even at noontime the room was a gloomy twilight, and today it was so crowded that the prisoners could scarcely move about. They were all Quakers, sent to Newgate for refusing to take an oath. "The law requires you to swear that your statements are true!" had thundered the officers of the court. "Nay," the Quakers had replied, "a man's word, truthfully given, is as binding as any oath can be, and it is wrong to swear." So they had all been herded into Newgate to spend months of imprisonment for this offense.

"Thomas, thou art taller than I. Canst thou reach the hook yonder to fasten my hammock?" called out an older man.

"Yes, indeed," answered Thomas, "but why not hang it to the post in the middle of the room to-night, in the place where poor James has been. That will be in the middle row, and the air may be better."

"James was a delicate man," replied the other as he acted on Thomas's advice; "it is not surprising that he died in this vile atmosphere, even though we gave him the best place that we could."

Everyone felt very much depressed by the death of this prisoner, and as they began to put up their hammocks, which had to be hung in all directions across the room, and one above the other until they were three rows high, the Friends still talked of him.

Suddenly there was a great noise of voices and tramping of feet outside. A key grated in the lock, and a torch threw a blinding light into the room as the turnkey opened the door and shouted, "Hold, hold! here is the coroner's inquest come to see you!"

A jury had come to inquire the reason for the death of the man. There was scarcely room for them to come in, so they crowded at the door. At last the foreman exclaimed, "What a sight is here! We need not now question how this man came by his death: we may rather wonder that they all are not dead, for this place is enough to breed an infection among them!"

The jury withdrew, and the Quakers thought no more of the affair until the next day. Then a sheriff came and explained that he wished that he could set them all free; but as that was not in his power, he would send a number of them to the old Bridewell Prison, which was less crowded. "This," he said, "will be more comfortable for you, and your removal will give more room to those left behind."

And now a very strange thing happened. The porter, who should have escorted them from one prison to the other, told them that as they knew the way to Bridewell, and as he could trust them, they might as well go there alone, provided they were in before bedtime! So Thomas Ellwood and some thirty more of the Friends made up their packs of clothing, and taking their bundles on their shoulders, walked two and two abreast from Newgate to old Bridewell. Some staggered slightly as from weakness, others stepped firmly as though their feet welcomed the good earth once more. The faces of all were pale from the confinement of the prison. They looked about them calmly, and often smiled to see the blue sky and smell the fresh air. It was the middle of the afternoon and the street was full of people. Shop-keepers stared from their doors and passers-by stopped the little procession to ask who they were and where they were going. They said that they were prisoners, going from one prison to another.

"What!" exclaimed the townsmen. "Without a keeper? Why don't you go home? This is your opportunity!"

"No," Thomas Ellwood answered proudly, "for our word, which we have given, is our keeper."

A BOOMERANG

"FRIEND Mouse-deer, will you be so good as to take care of my children while I go fishing," said the Otter.

"To be sure I will," agreed the Mouse-deer; but no sooner had the Otter departed than the Woodpecker began beating on his War-drum.

Now the Mouse-deer was chief dancer of the War-dance so when he heard the War-drum he *had* to dance and he forgot all about the Otter's children and danced upon them with his sharp little hoofs and killed them all.

By and by the Otter returned with a big string of cray fish and when he found his babies all dead, he went to King Solomon and prostrating himself, said:

"Oh King, hear my story. The Mouse-deer has killed all of my children. Is he or is he not guilty according to the law of the land?"

And King Solomon replied:

"If the Mouse-deer hath done this thing wittingly, assuredly he is guilty."

And he sent for the Mouse-deer and asked:

"Was it your doing that the Otter's children were killed?"

"Assuredly it was," replied the Mouse-deer, "but it was not my fault. The Woodpecker sounded the War-drum and I am chief dancer of the War-dance and I *had* to dance and as I danced I trod on the Otter's children."

"Send for the Woodpecker," ordered the King.

"Was it you, Woodpecker, who sounded the War-gong?"

"Assuredly it was," said the Woodpecker, "I *had* to for I saw the Great Lizard wearing his sword."

Then the King commanded the Great Lizard to be summoned.

"Is it true, Lizard, you were wearing your sword?"

"Assuredly it is, your Majesty, I *had* to because I saw that the Tortoise had donned his coat of mail."

"Send for the Tortoise," commanded the King.

"Did you, Tortoise, don your coat of mail?"

"Assuredly I did," replied the Tortoise, "I *had* to because I saw the King-crab trailing his three-edged pike."

Then the King-crab was sent for.

"Did you, King-crab, come trailing your three-edged pike?"

"Assuredly I did, I *had* to because the Cray-fish had shouldered his lance."

Then the King sent for the Cray-fish and demanded:

"Were you, Cray-fish, shouldering your lance?"

"Assuredly I was, your Majesty, I had to."

"And why did you have to?"

"Because, your Majesty, I saw the Otter coming down to devour my children."

"Then," said the King, "the Otter is to blame. It was the Otter who killed the Otter's children for this is the law of the land."

Retold from Fables and Folk Tales from an Eastern Forest *by Walter Skeat.*

THE WHITE FEATHER

"ALL that I can say, man, is that you are crazy to risk it!"

Little Joseph Newlin ran to the door of the cabin to see who dared speak thus to his father. He thought he recognized the voice of a neighbor, Samuel Fuller, and was amazed to find that he was right. Samuel stood beside a cart, which was piled high with a queer array of household goods. Perched on the top, on a mattress, sat Samuel's wife and Joshua, their little boy.

"Hello, Josh!" piped Joseph, but Joshua only answered with an angry glare, very like neighbor Samuel's. Joseph was tremendously hurt and puzzled. He ran to his father, who glanced down at his son with his usual loving serenity. He continued, however, to talk to neighbor Samuel.

"I cannot feel as thee does, Samuel, and I am firmly convinced that I am doing right. For years we Quakers—and you, too, Samuel, thee and the others, have seemed to agree with us—we have said that so long as we ourselves acted and felt toward the red men as toward human brothers, they would not harm us. Now, at the first hint of danger——" (Father's voice made Joseph tremble and yet feel strangely proud) "thee and the others forget all you have professed, and flee in unworthy terror——"

"'Unworthy terror' indeed! Thomas Newlin, how can you say it! I tell you, Kentville was burnt to the ground last night—not a man, woman or child remain—and the red savages dance their war-dance upon the ashes. From every side we have heard tales of murder and ravage. The Indians are on the war-path, and at any moment may descend upon Cincinnati. We are among the last to leave the town. The Hillers have just preceded us—'Unworthy terror!'

126

You know not what you are saying!" Under the blazing and contemptuous eyes of Samuel Fuller, little Joseph clung close to his father's legs.

"Pardon me, Samuel, I realize well what I am saying. In Kentville the white people were fully armed and long ago roused the enmity of the Indians by suspicious, harsh treatment of their red brothers. Thee wastes words upon me, neighbor. Thy indignation grieves me, but much more it grieves me that we, of all the twenty families in the settlement of Cincinnati, are the only ones who will risk a test of our Christian principles. Do not think my wife and I have not thought of the danger our course involves. We are ready—so are little Sarah, and Joseph, here."

Samuel Fuller turned away with a look of speechless contempt. Then he paused again.

"Thomas, are you armed?"

"I am not—nor wish to be."

"You are mad!"

Joseph gasped and looked quickly at his father. With unruffled countenance the man stood gazing down the deserted street after the retreating cart, on the top of which balanced little Joshua. Anger filled Joseph's heart, and then all at once he felt unaccountably lonely. Though he tried hard to smother it, a hateful sob escaped him. Father leaned down quickly and gathered him into his arms.

"This is not the time to be sad, little son, but joyous and brave! Come, let us see what Mother and Sarah are doing."

Mother was spinning, and little Sarah was begging to be allowed to go blackberrying. Berries grew thick in the pasture back of the house, on the edge of the vast forest that surrounded the settlement of Cincinnati. "Let me go, too," cried Joseph, forgetting his misery.

Mother glanced at Father with an odd, questioning look, almost as though she were frightened. But immediately the look vanished as Father said, "Certainly they may go, Mother. Listen, children; forget not at any time, if Indians approach you, to speak courteously to them, as to our neighbors, and invite them for rest and refreshment to our home. They are our friends."

"Of course, Father," piped Sarah, and the two children ran off merrily to get the pail.

In a very few days Joseph and Sarah became quite used to being without other playfellows than each other. The street, with its empty houses from which all the neighbors had fled, made them feel queer, so they spent much time with Father in the fields, or playing near Mother in the kitchen. Occasionally a white man, always carrying a gun, would hurry through the village, stop as if amazed at the sight of them, talk in low, excited tones to Father, and hurry on again. But Father was never excited.

One morning Father was filling the wood-box and had just entered the kitchen, when Joseph, standing idly at the door, saw an Indian step out of the forest across the pasture —and after him another and another. "Father, come see!" he called, and together they stood in the doorway and watched a long line of red men, painted, feathered and carrying curious knives, clubs and tomahawks, thread their way across the field.

"Wife, our red brothers are approaching," said Father quietly, and Mother came to watch them, her hand on Father's arm. Sarah jumped up and squealed with pleasure at the bright glitter of the beads they wore and the tall feathers in their hair. Joseph gazed at their dark faces and wondered why they looked so fierce and angry. They turned neither to right nor left, but came straight toward the cabin, each man clutching a tomahawk.

When the first Indian had reached the little patch of

grass around the house, Father stepped forward, his hand extended.

"Good day, brothers," he said in his kind, courteous voice.

The first Indian stopped suddenly, and all back of him halted as at a signal. The leader glanced at the open hand, but did not touch it. ("That is rude," thought Joseph.) The Indian looked at Mother smiling a welcome in the doorway, and at little Sarah and Joseph. When the black eyes met his, Joseph felt a little tremor of excitement run up the calves of his legs and his backbone, but it was not fear. The Indian pushed past Mother, the whole line following, and they crowded into the kitchen. Their moccasined feet turned up the edge of Mother's plaited rag rug, and Joseph darted to straighten it, but Father laid a restraining hand on his shoulder.

The Indian turned to Father. "Guns," he muttered very deep in his throat. Father spread out both hands: "None," he answered. Then with a gesture toward the best parlor and the stairs, "Go look."

The Indians trooped out of the kitchen into the hall, all except one, who remained standing at the outside doorway. Joseph set the rug to rights. Mother put wood in the stove and lifted the jug of molasses down from the shelf. Sarah stared at the Indian with fascinated eyes.

"Joseph," said Mother, "I think it likely that they are hungry. Bring the large loaf and the butter from the vault."

Joseph hurried eagerly, and by the time he had climbed up again from the vault with the butter, the kitchen was again full of Indians.

"Eat?" Father was saying questioningly, pointing to the bread and jug. Joseph was astonished at the change in the behavior of these men. Broad smiles spread over their faces, and instead of silence, they uttered queer, uncouth grunts and words that had no sense to a white boy's ears. One Indian grabbed the loaf and tore it to pieces with his hands, rapidly distributing great hunks among the others. Another seized the jug and poured the molasses on the bread, dribbling much upon the floor, as it passed from one to another. The neat pat of butter they bit into with their teeth as though it had been cheese. Sarah exclaimed at this in horror, but Mother silenced her.

And then—as suddenly as they had come—they were out of the kitchen and down the path. Mother, Father and the children hurried to the door to watch them go. Joseph thought he saw his mother wipe something from her eyes, and Father slipped his arm around her waist. At the edge of the woods the Indians, instead of disappearing, seated themselves in a circle on the ground. Mother stiffened suddenly, and Sarah asked, "Are the Indians tired, Father?" Father did not answer. He was watching them closely. One Indian stood in the center and talked excitedly, throwing his arms around a great deal and pointing often toward the house. Now and then he was interrupted by a chorus of grunts, in protest or agreement—it was impossible to tell which. As the little group at the doorway watched breathlessly, Joseph felt for the second time the shiver run up his legs and back.

The Indians settled into silence for a moment. Then one of their number—he who had led the line—sprang up and ran toward the house, a long white feather in his hand. The feather curved gracefully, and Joseph longed to smooth it. The Indian reached the doorway—his face was no longer dark and stern. "Ugh—brother—paleface," he said, with a large gesture which Joseph knew was meant for one of friendliness.

Quickly and deftly the Indian stuck the quill in the crack above the doorway, so that the feather stood upright, beautiful and glistening white in the sunshine. When Joseph turned from admiring it, not a sign of an Indian was to be seen. The place where they had sat was deserted, and he saw only his father and mother holding one another's hands quite tightly. Sarah was dancing up and down below the feather.

"It is the Indians' sign of peace," said Father. "All red men will respect it. Even so they have respected the peace in our hearts, to which we have been steadfast."

WILLIAM ANSWERS A LETTER

"WHAT a night!" thought William as he and the young American walked along under the southern sky, bright with moonlight, the air soft and fragrant with honeysuckle and other wonderful smells he couldn't identify. Just to breathe seemed a pleasure over here. He'd miss England, of course, but to be twenty-three and across the ocean on your first job—helping to build a railroad—was thrilling.

"I'm in the United States," he went on to himself as though he couldn't believe it. "Came pretty nearly not being united, though."

He had wanted so much to come to America after he'd finished his engineering course and had followed the news of the great Civil War between the states with as much interest as if it had been his own country. Would the war ever end? It had seemed to his family, peace-loving Quakers and Abolitionists, an especially evil thing. First, that men could own other human beings just like horses or cattle, or that, later, part of one country could fight with another part like two brothers in one family.

But now that was all over, the bitterness and hatred. How meaningless the words of the Chief Engineer had sounded:

"As you value your life, Thompson," he had said, "don't let anybody know that you are a Quaker or an abolitionist."

"A penny for your thoughts," broke in his companion.

With a start William realized he hadn't said a word to his newly-made friend, not since they had had that wonderful swim back there in the mill pond.

"I'm sorry. I was thinking about it over here. How kind

132

you've been, you and everyone else on the job, everyone I've met. It's a wonderfully friendly country."

"Yes, well—I hope," his friend stopped abruptly and there was an uncomfortable feeling in the air, almost as though a disagreeable third person had joined them. William looked at his companion who walked along with his head down. They continued in silence, their feet making no sound in the velvet soft dust of the road. The trees, thickly hung with Spanish moss, arched overhead, shutting out the moonlight. Where the road branched they were about to take the fork which led directly back to the village when suddenly they were stopped dead in their tracks. Just ahead, where the moonlight fell full upon him through a gap in the trees, a ghostly figure on a horse appeared seemingly from nowhere. From head to feet horse and rider were draped in calico, only their eyes showing like black spots through holes in the covering. The young men stopped abruptly. Then William walked ahead to investigate the hooded figure. It was real all right. The horse snorted, then tossed its head jingling its bridle. The mounted figure silently raised its arm and pointed to the other fork in the road. William looked around for his friend but he had already turned back and was motioning with his head for William to follow. So this wasn't a joke. His friend was evidently frightened. All the more reason to go ahead and see what this was all about. But when the man on horseback drew his pistol and pointed it directly at him, William decided the only thing he could do was to follow his friend.

"What's going on here?" William asked when he had caught up.

"I don't know what you're talking about." His friend looked straight ahead.

"Oh, now, you saw him. Why are we taking this round-about way back?"

Then the friend realizing that William was not to be put off, stopped and in a voice so low that it could scarcely be heard, replied,

"If you want to stay alive, you've seen nothing. Don't ever mention it again."

As they neared the house where William lived they met two acquaintances and William, hoping to avert a danger he felt to be abroad, started to tell them of their recent experience. A hand was instantly clamped over his mouth and another gripped his shoulder.

"Listen, we're your friends, believe us, but you didn't see a thing, *not a thing*. Don't mention this to anyone."

The young men said brief goodnights to him at the door and William let himself in completely mystified and more than a little hurt by his friends' attitude. But he wasn't going to let the matter rest there. He would find out; and seeing a light in the little sitting-room at the end of the hall he went directly to it. His landlady, a motherly soul who had been his friend and counselor ever since his arrival, was alone.

"Good evening, William." She looked up smiling. Then seeing his troubled face, "Is something the matter?"

But as he described the white-clothed figure her face paled and she put her finger to her lip and shook her head to stop him.

"Come in and close the door. I'll tell you about this though I'm sorry you have to know."

She pulled down the curtain and motioning him to sit beside her on the sofa explained that the white robed figure on the horse was a sentinel of the Ku Klux Klan. The Klan was probably right now about its terrible business on that stretch of road back there.

She told him that the feelings of violence had not abated entirely when the war ended and some Southerners, smarting from defeat had resorted to this growing secret group that rode at night, disguised, and was a law unto itself. There seemed to be no one to whom the respectable people who deplored and feared the Klan could appeal. You were always hushed up if you ever mentioned it. Your next-door neighbor might be a member. It was rumored that the sheriff and his men . . . but she didn't know.

"I'm sorry I had to tell you. I'm ashamed. But you had to know for your own protection. Please, please, don't speak of this to anyone."

He said goodnight with a heavy heart. In this friendly land could such things happen?

The next day he heard that a well known Negro, a blacksmith, living on that road, had "left the country" and people spoke in hushed tones of his widow. No one would give evidence; not even the widow or her children made any reply when questioned.

Days went by full of hard absorbing work for William. People were as cordial and friendly as ever and it had begun to seem almost as though all the unpleasantness had been a bad dream when an incident took place that brought the tension and high feeling back in full force.

An invitation came from the General to a ball in honor of his daughter. William did not dance but since the General was president of the railroad an invitation from him was practically a command. Besides, he appreciated the cordiality and accepted with real anticipation.

The gay and lively scene, so foreign to anything in his sober background, held him in a kind of happy daze, until suddenly during an intermission, when the musicians were resting, the group in which William was standing began rather heatedly to talk of abolition.

"If there is one set of people on earth for whom I have unmitigated horror, loathing, and contempt," said the General's daughter, "it is the Quaker Abolitionists of England who, safe enough themselves, egged on and helped the Quakers in this country."

Then noticing his silence she turned to William.

"Mr. Thompson, you have not said a word on the subject. As a Northerner, what do you think of them?"

William swallowed and then in the calmest voice he could muster, said:

"After your last remark it is difficult for me to reply. I am myself an English Quaker Abolitionist."

It was a bombshell. The group moved off leaving William stranded. He saw them in eager discussion with the others. Presently they returned, having clearly made some plan. The General's daughter came up to him and apologized for her remarks, saying she had, of course, not known who he was. One of the number then proposed:

"Since none of us has ever heard the Quakers spoken of except with scorn, perhaps, Mr. Thompson, you will give us the other side of the question."

"With great pleasure . . ."

"Then we will give you a hearing," said a deep voice behind him and clapping his hands for quiet, the General announced to the entire assembly,

"We have with us an English Quaker Abolitionist who will now give us in a speech, not exceeding a quarter of an hour, a defence of his people. The dancing will stop and I will consider it a personal affront if anyone interrupts the speaker. Now, Mr. Thompson, go up into the rostrum."

William went up, his heart in his mouth. But as he looked down on the assembly, he felt that courage was suddenly given to him so that he was able to present his case in a clear and calm manner.

He felt no animosity toward these people. They simply did not understand. He ended by saying his people believed that all men were brothers, black and white, and that there was that of God in every man.

Two days later three men whom he thought he recognized as having been at the ball, came to him and said they were sent by a very important society to find out exactly what his opinions on slavery were.

"If you were at the ball," William replied, "you have already got your answer."

"That will not do," said the spokesman, "we represent a very important society and have orders to take down the information direct."

"Then you may tell your very important society to mind their own business and I will mind mine."

After dinner when William went to his room he saw, pinned on the window sill, a letter directed to Mr. William Phillips Thompson. It had a skull and cross-bones on one side, a railroad train on the other and below were the words:

YOU ARE REQUESTED TO LEAVE THE STATE WITHIN 24 HOURS OR WE WILL NOT BE RESPONSIBLE FOR YOUR LIFE.
BY ORDER OF THE COUNCIL. K.K.K.

"How did I ever get into this fix?" said William to himself. "Here I am with a splendid job which I don't want to lose. I can't run away at the sight of a skull and cross-bones. What ought I to do?"

He prayed for guidance and almost immediately he felt it strongly laid upon him to go at once to the town square and publicly defy the Ku Klux Klan.

He hurried to the square. Just in front of the post-office he saw a high barrel on end and two boxes for steps leading to it. He mounted it and waving his letter attracted a crowd.

At the same moment several men in tall hats came out of the post-office. They were evidently making their way to the hotel, but seeing the crowd and being curious to know what was afoot they turned back to listen.

William was exhibiting the letter and shouting:

"If there are any Ku Klux here present (and I am quite sure there are), I wish them to give my replies to their Council's message. I will *not* leave the state within twenty-four hours, but tonight at 8 o'clock, unarmed as I always am, I will go outside the town and round the Lutheran Church, which is the most lonely place I can think of, and if any Ku Klux desire to meet me let them come."

He climbed off the barrel; the crowd dispersed and the men in tall hats proceeded to the hotel.

One of his acquaintances whispered to him when nobody was near "You are going to your grave."

At three o'clock the General's son called with a letter from his father saying that William must leave by the night train and that an escort would be provided to take him to the station, the General guaranteeing safe conduct to beyond the state line and giving him a free pass.

William thanked him. He said he did not feel it right to leave but must stay and see it through.

Too nervous to eat any supper, he became so weak and trembling that by quarter of eight he could hardly walk. Nevertheless he went out to keep his appointment. There on the steps outside the door he found the General's son and a knot of young men who had come to take him to the station. How hard they were making it for him! But he stuck to his purpose, gratefully refusing their offer. Then he started out in the other direction. It was pitch dark. As he felt his way by the corners of the fences, he began wondering what he should say if he were challenged. Suddenly the words of the gospels came to him:

"If you are brought before rulers and kings, take no thought what ye shall say, for it shall be told you in that hour what you ought to say."

Strengthened and encouraged he had proceeded three quarters of the way around the church when he heard a harsh voice,

"Halt! Who goes there?"

"I, William Phillips Thompson."

He could feel several men surround him in the dark.

"What do you mean by defying the Ku Klux Klan?"

"What do you mean by ordering me to leave the state? Have I not as much right here as you have?"

They seemed surprised at such defiance. The spokesman continued:

"We know that you are a spy for the Governor."

"I am no spy, and did not even know the name of the Governor until I saw the proclamation on the wall of the Court House today. I have my credentials with me and will hand them to you if you will promise to give them back."

Snatching the papers they went off to read them, leaving one of their number with his pistol pointed at William's head.

"You are a dead man if you move."

They were gone a long time. At last they came back and took away the first man while another stood guard. When they returned a voice out of the darkness announced:

"Your credentials are as you said. If you will leave the state tomorrow we will let you off."

"I refuse to go."

They conferred again.

"We don't want to execute you, and will let you off if you will make public recantation of Quakerism and Abolitionism tomorrow in the same place where you read the letter."

"I refuse to do so."

They conferred again.

"What do you propose?" they asked.

"I have no desire to interfere with your institutions," William replied. "I would not have said anything if my opinion had not been asked. I only want to be allowed to do the work for which I came."

There followed more discussion.

"Will you promise not to run for political office, not to attend negro meetings, or to assist negro insurrection?"

"I have no desire to do any of those things."

"Then give us back our letter in exchange for your credentials."

The exchange was made, they shook hands and William, half-dead from the experience, dragged himself back to his lodging house.

The next day he had a high fever and of the days following he remembered very little. Kind hands brought him cool cloths for his forehead and soup when he was able to eat.

When he recovered no one ever asked him what had happened, not even his devoted landlady.

Several months later, however, it began to be rumored that people were betraying the Ku Klux Klan. Everybody was in a state of panic for very many had joined from fear of the threats of the K.K.K. if they held off. One day after the excitement had died down, the Governor of the State sent for William and told him that within an hour of his public defiance the Government had been informed about it.

"I took it for granted that you would be murdered," he said. "I thought that if you were, I should at any rate get my opportunity to pin something on them and declare martial law. Do you know what saved you?"

"No."

"Did you see those dozen or so men with tall hats and staves?"

"Yes."

"They were a Radical Committee of the State and the K.K.K. knew that they would report to me what you intended to do and that for once the State would have definite evidence against the Klan. If it had not been for those men coming out when they did, your life would not have been worth a cent."

Later William moved off up-country to superintend the building of his railway. Everywhere he went he found that the story of his challenging the Ku Klux Klan had preceded him. It brought him a reputation for toughness invaluable to a man who never carried arms, and whose work lay among rough men ready to shoot on the smallest provocation.

Note: William Phillips Thompson 1846-1926. Went to Bootham School, York; became an engineer and went to the United States. Later settled as a Patent Agent in Liverpool, his native town. The events in this story are as he recorded them.

THE LATCHSTRING

"WELL, perhaps we ought at least to bar our door, for the sake of the children." Mary Tyler spoke reluctantly, and there was a note of uncertainty in her voice.

"Perhaps so," replied James Tyler. "It seems to me every man within five miles has upbraided me for not protecting my children."

Mary glanced with troubled eyes at the face of her husband, as they sat before the fire in their little cabin. She knew that he, too, was living over the uncertain days since the outbreak of the war. Time and again there had been reports that the British soldiers had incited the Indians to burn the cabins of the settlers and massacre whole families. Despite these reports, the Tylers had lived, as before, on friendly terms with their neighbors, both Indians and white men. When massacres had occurred in nearby settlements, they had still continued to leave out the latchstring, that leather thong which enabled a person outside the door to lift the latch and enter.

The Tylers had trusted entirely to the protection of their Heavenly Father, and had refused to arm themselves, or even to lock their door. Now they had reliable assurance that the Indians were coming to destroy their settlement. Neighbors urged that they had no right to imperil the lives of their children by such foolhardiness—that they should protect themselves.

"But is it really protection?" Mary queried, as now they sat alone in their cabin.

"At least," responded James, "we shall be doing what most people consider safest."

For what seemed a long time, they sat gazing at the fire.

The silence was broken only by the moaning of the wind in the pine trees and the crackling of the logs on the hearth. For the first time in all the dark days, Mary felt afraid. She stirred uneasily and cast a furtive glance around the shadowy room. James rose and lighted a candle. He crossed the room and stood for a moment uncertainly beside the outside door. Then, with a deep sigh, he pulled in the leather thong, fastened the latch securely, and prepared for bed.

All night James tossed restlessly. Every time one of the children stirred, or a branch scraped the roof, he would start violently, and fall back unnerved. He tried to calm himself by repeating verses from the Bible, but instead of the usual comfort, the words only brought a challenge to his excited brain. "Why are ye fearful, O ye of little faith?" "Take the shield of faith, wherewith ye shall be able to quench all the fiery darts of the wicked."

"Mary," he whispered at last, "art thou awake?"

"Yes, James," she replied, "I have not slept. I have tried to pray, and always the answer has been, 'Behold the Lord's hand is not shortened that it can not save.'"

"Thou art right, Mary, the Lord's hand is not shortened and we did wrong to pull in the latchstring. Shall we put our trust entirely in Him?"

"Aye, James, I should feel much safer so," she replied.

Quickly James stepped to the door and pulled the leather thong through to the outside. Then he lay down again and both enjoyed such a sense of peace and security as they had not felt for hours. Suddenly, just as they were about to drop off to sleep, they heard a blood-curdling war-whoop. A few seconds later the moccasined footsteps of several men passed the window and stopped in front of the door. The latch clicked and the door swung open. By the dim light from the embers on the hearth, James could see seven Indians in full war paint. They motioned and talked to each other and then silently pulled the door to and disappeared into the night.

In the morning, when James and Mary looked out of their door, they saw only the smoking ruins of their neighbors' cabins.

Years later, when the war was over, the government of the United States appointed James Tyler as a representative to an Indian conference. One day he told this story to all those assembled. In reply, an Indian arose and said: "I was one of those Indians. We crept up in night. We meant to burn and kill. We found latchstring out. We said, 'No burn this house. No kill these people. They do us no harm. They trust Great Spirit.'"

THE LION-MAKERS

IN A certain town were four Brahmans who lived in friendship. Three of them had reached the far shore of all scholarship, but lacked sense. The other found scholarship distasteful; he had nothing but sense.

One day they met for consultation. "What is the use of attainments," said they, "if one does not travel, win the favor of kings, and acquire money? Whatever we do, let us all travel."

But when they had gone a little way, the eldest of them said: "One of us, the fourth, is a dullard, having nothing but sense. Now nobody gains the favorable attention of kings by simple sense without scholarship. Therefore we will not share our earnings with him. Let him turn back and go home."

Then the second said: "My intelligent friend, you lack scholarship. Please go home." But the third said: "No, no. This is no way to behave. For we have played together since we were little boys. Come along, my noble friend. You shall have a share of the money we earn."

With this agreement they continued their journey, and in a forest they found the bones of a dead lion. Thereupon one of them said: "A good opportunity to test the ripeness of our scholarship. Here lies some kind of creature, dead. Let us bring it to life by means of the scholarship we have honestly won."

Then the first said: "I know how to assemble the skeleton." The second said: "I can supply skin, flesh, and blood." The third said: "I can give it life."

So the first assembled the skeleton, the second provided skin, flesh, and blood. But while the third was intent on giving the breath of life, the man of sense advised against it, remarking: "This is a lion. If you bring him to life, he will kill every one of us."

"You simpleton!" said the other, "it is not I who will reduce scholarship to a nullity." "In that case," came the reply, "wait a moment, while I climb this convenient tree."

When this had been done, the lion was brought to life, rose up, and killed all three. But the man of sense, after the lion had gone elsewhere, climbed down and went home.

This story retold from The Panchatantra *is used with the permission of the translator, Arthur W. Ryder. Copyright 1925 by the University of Chicago Press.*

HOLY GROUND

TITITITITITITITITITITITITITITITITITITITI

It was the week before Christmas. Crowds of merry people were jostling each other in the shopping district of a London suburb. Joan was happy to be in the middle of the excitement with her grandmother who had come over from Germany.

"Oh look, Granny," she cried pointing to a sign flashing in the sky. WE BELIEVE IN ENGLAND. "Isn't that wonderful? So do I."

Later walking home over the big bridge, Joan said with a friendly tug at her grandmother's hand, "So sorry, Granny, you can't believe in England because you are German. But you believe in Germany, don't you?"

"Yes, Joanie, in a way, but I believe in something more, and tonight I will tell you about it."

When Joan was tucked in bed, her grandmother told her the following story:

Some years ago, before you were born, there lived a little boy in Germany whose name was Hartmut. He hadn't any brothers or sisters and his parents were rather old. So he spent most of his time with boys and girls of his own age. You can imagine how much fun they had together. When he was ten years old he and all the other boys and girls became members of the Hitler-Youth. He liked it very much; he loved his smart uniform; he felt very proud and grown-up when he had to take the oath to Germany and her Führer. He really believed in Germany. It seemed just wonderful to live in those years! Everywhere he saw busy people and his father who had been out of work for a long time had a good job again. He saw majestic streets being built for all those new cars, and very often he loitered on one of the new bridges which swung over the Autobahn to marvel at the traffic. Whenever he came to town he saw enormous new buildings shooting up like mushrooms. He loved it when the police stopped the traffic to let the Hitler-Youth march along, four abreast with banners and drums. Sometimes he would stand for hours and hours in a line with other boys and girls in uniform waiting for one of the new politicians or even Hitler himself to pass by. WE BELIEVE IN GERMANY, that was written with letters of fire before his mind and that was the never ending theme when he addressed his young followers at the camp fires in the evening, for Hartmut had become a leader himself now.

Just before the war Hartmut was allowed to go to the Balkans with some of the other young leaders. They went down the Danube, a wonderful river; they saw Vienna, the old Austrian capital with her palaces full of historical memories as well as of music. And on they went in their boat to the south-east. Wide, wide, open spaces spread before their eyes; they saw shepherds on horseback with wide cloaks floating behind them like wings; they saw clouds of dust raised by hundreds of horses, clouds which changed the blue of the sky into a dirty yellowish gray and which became purple after sunset as if gigantic fires were burning in the west. Sometimes children were standing near the shore with brown faces and dark hair and they were ragged and dirty. That was in the Balkans, so different from Germany which seemed very far away. But they carried the idea of their country in their hearts; they never lost it and the more they saw those strange, dark poor people on the shore of the big river, the clearer they saw Germany. Germany, that meant cleanliness, order, straightforwardness, marching, rhythm, power. They marched through the foreign towns with their heads up, proud. Above the noisy, smelly streets, they visioned the golden letters, WE BELIEVE IN GERMANY.

And then there was war, and each country put up big boards to make it quite clear: WE BELIEVE IN ENGLAND—WE BELIEVE IN FRANCE—IN GERMANY, IN ITALY, AMERICA, HOLLAND, NORWAY, JAPAN, CHINA . . .

Of course Hartmut wanted to be a soldier. He was too young when war started but two years later he joined the army and after some training went to the east, to Russia.

It was winter, a very stormy, hard winter, and the world lay buried under deep, deep snow. For days and days he traveled through white endless woods; then through open land where the small towns and villages were almost buried in snow. All he could see was the blue smoke curling out of chimneys and the churches with their typical onion on top of the spire. After a while Hartmut left the train for a sledge. Slowly, very slowly, the horses went on, steaming and trembling with exhaustion. Here a pole to mark the way; there a pole; woods again, and at last they arrived.

War and cold had driven both the German and the Russian armies underground and they lived as people did thousands of years ago. But it was not too bad in those holes, Hartmut thought. An iron stove heated the room, the wood crackled, sparks flew around like fire flies and small oil lamps enlarged the shadows of people and things and set them trembling on the walls.

It was quite a peaceful life that Hartmut met. He had longed for big marches, battles and victories in which he might get a medal but his only duty was to patrol a broad strip of land, No-man's land, on the other side of which the Russians lived their molelike lives. During the daytime those patrols were easy. There was always something to be seen in the wide, white world, some far hills, the debris of woods, small black spots out of the chimneys of which curled the spicy smell of wood fires.

But during the nights Hartmut felt as if he were transported into a strange and dangerous world. He sometimes felt absolutely lost even when he was quite near their shelters. Then he seemed to see hills rise before his eyes which he never had noticed during the daytime, or the spires of a big town lying under the glittering cold stars. Then again he heard all sorts of noises, somebody walking, murmuring behind his back—and when he spun around— he was alone under the majestic night sky.

After some time his nerves became steadier and he got used to this sort of life and land. Then he walked up and down with his white shirt pulled over his cloak, and sometimes went far into No-man's land, hoping for some adventures with the enemy he hated so bitterly. But nothing ever seemed to happen and after two hours on duty he would creep back to sleep under his blanket while one of his comrades, another white figure, disappeared into the night.

One night he was on duty between twelve and two. It was terribly cold. An icy storm swept the snow up in clouds; his face burned, his ears hummed and he could scarcely keep his eyes open. It was not very dark for the moon was nearly full. Hartmut trotted on and cursed his life. He stamped his feet to keep them warm, pulled his shawl deep over his eyes and ears and put his hands in his pockets. The path he was following suddenly disappeared; the storm had heaped up great walls of snow and Hartmut stumbled like a drunken man. On and on he trudged. The cold was making him sleepy and he bit his lip to keep himself awake. He tried to reason out from the position of the moon which direction was "home" but his head swam and his ears roared and he couldn't think. His longing for sleep was so intense that when he stumbled and fell he made no effort to get up.

*   *   *

When Hartmut opened his eyes he was in a small dug-out and a dark haired young man was bending over him. Suddenly the expression of anxiety in the young man's eyes changed to joy. He threw up his hands and said something in a strange language. Hartmut sat up and looked around. He felt as if he were in a dream. In a flash he remembered all he had ever heard about the Russians how cruel they were, more animal than human. And here was this Russian smiling at him. He glanced around. Nobody else was there. A small stove glowed. Two logs were put beside it for seats.

The young Russian's face was lighted by a candle which was burning in the neck of a bottle.

"How did I get here?" Hartmut asked in sign language and the other enacted in pantomine how he had found him unconscious and dragged him in.

"Hartmut," said the German pointing to himself.

"Mischka," said the Russian pointing to himself.

The fire in the little wood stove made a cheerful glow but it was not so warm as the light in Mischka's face. While he prepared a cup of steaming hot sweet tea to give to his enemy-friend, Mischka talked with a soft and singing voice which made the winter night into a fairy tale. Hartmut's heart filled with warmth. There grew during those minutes what he had never experienced before, a strong simple love without asking anything, just growing and flowering and warming his heart and mind.

Then Hartmut became conscious of real life again. It was time to leave. Mischka led him up some narrow steps which came out under a gigantic, uprooted pine tree. With the grace and sureness of a young animal, Mischka piloted him across No-man's land to within a short distance of the German lines.

Here they paused and smiled good-bye.

Suddenly Mischka ran back, pointed to the dial of his wrist watch and with unmistakable gestures asked, "Come again?"

Hartmut understood and hesitated. But then he nodded, showed the time, 2-4 on the dial of his watch, and Mischka sped away through the snow.

Hartmut lay on his bunk among the German soldiers without sleep, deep in thought. Had he done wrong, had he brought danger to his fellows, had he acted as a traitor against Germany? WE BELIEVE IN GERMANY—he tried to cling to those words; they had been the compass throughout his life, but ever and ever again he felt them slip away and then he saw the good and smiling face of Mischka, heard his soft strange voice and felt his warm, strong hand.

He pictured one of the Russian huts—he had seen hundreds of them: dirty, half broken down, chickens, goat, pig, and people crammed together in the same room—perhaps Mischka's home looked exactly like that. It was madness to think of him as he did with the strong feeling of friendship—madness—madness—but he struggled in vain, the clear eyes smiled at him blotting out the letters, we believe in Germany.

They met again the following night and Hartmut had some cigarettes and a small bar of his chocolate ration for their meeting.

Time and again they met and then came the end: One night—perhaps they had not been careful enough—suddenly a bright rocket sailed over their heads and another one followed. They flopped down on the ground, but already a machine gun had started its tak, tak, tak, and suddenly Hartmut felt a blow and terrible pain in his foot. Mischka heard him moan and quickly came to his aid. Carefully he tried to undo the boot, and when he saw the pain in Hartmut's face he cut off the boot and fixed his handkerchief around the foot with soft consoling words which made Hartmut smile through his pain. Then Mischka tucked his friend up with his cloak and turned to go. In the same moment he collapsed beside Hartmut; the machine gun had got him. The warm hands became cold.

Hartmut was brought home an hour later after all had become quiet again. When they found him beside the dead Russian soldier they asked him if he had shot him. Then he probably would get the iron cross. But Hartmut only shook his head. When he was put on a sledge on some straw and sent westward—home—he cried as he never had cried in his life.

"Don't cry, Joanie, dear, think how wonderful this friendship had been for both of them even if it did not last long. It was Hartmut, himself, who told me the story one evening when the wireless was preaching the gospel to millions, WE BELIEVE IN GERMANY. Now you will understand why Hartmut couldn't listen."

"But what did he believe in, Granny?"

"He believed in love, dear heart, and there is nothing else. You will learn it, too, when you are growing up."

"And now if you will go to sleep quickly, I will tell you the end of the story. You remember the small dugout where they met? It had become holy ground, and the big pine tree, the roots of which first gave shelter to Hartmut and Mischka's friendship is blessed by God.

"During each Holy Night it stands again in full majesty

on the white endless plain of Russia under the wide sky with all the millions of stars. Then people who feel the holy ground under their feet will see candles on the tree with their soft warm shine, even in the worst snow storms, and they will hear some distant but clear music from above and can understand the words—each in his own language:

> Glory to God in the highest,
> And on earth peace,
> Good will toward men.

Grete Paquin-Gallwitz

THE SQUIRE'S HALF-CROWN

THE farmhouse kitchen was principally lighted by a blazing wood fire on a dark autumn Sunday evening more than a hundred years ago. On the table stood a rushlight —not a candle, but a peeled rush, which had been dipped in grease, and was held in iron pinchers. It was well that the farmer's great Bible was large print, as he drew up to the table to give his elder children their weekly Bible lesson, while mother put the little ones to bed.

"Little Pollie shall sit on my knee," he said, "and thou, Johnnie, shalt find the place. Turn to the first book of the New Testament, my boy—and Martin, canst thou tell me what Roman letters stand for seven?"

"V, I, I," answered Martin, who, although only ten, was an unusually intelligent lad.

"That's right—find the chapter, and Pollie knows the figures one and two, which makes twelve, so she can find the verse, and you shall each read it through. Now, Johnnie."

Johnnie was eleven, and he managed in a sing-song way to read correctly, "Wherefore whatsoever ye would that men should do to you, do ye even so to them."

Martin read more slowly, but with an accent, that showed he had some glimmering of the meaning, and the little sister, who as yet had had no schooling but what her busy parents could give her, managed to stumble through the verse after her brothers.

"Don't do anything thou would'st not like others to do to thee—put thyself in their place—eh, John, if thou wert a little girl, thou would'st not like thy hair pulled?" John, who had just given a brotherly tweak to Pollie's thick

155

mane, looked rather sheepish—he really had not imagination enough to fancy himself a girl.

"And if Pollie were the younger sister would she not like big Sallie to let her nurse the wooden baby?" went on the father smiling, and then slowly and carefully he taught the verse word by word until, when Mother came down, all three could repeat it. They then said over the verses learned on previous First-day evenings, and were soon dispatched to bed, for early hours prevailed at the farmhouse.

It was hardly daylight next morning before John and Martin had to start for school. There was no day-school within reach, so they boarded at Ifield Meeting House during the week, as a clever old cripple taught a number of boys in that village. "Teacher Sam," as his pupils called him, was a real enthusiast for education, and there was far less of the cane and more intelligent teaching than was often found in the village school in the early nineteenth century. The well-trained, obedient little Quaker boys were rather favourites of his, although they had to sit apart while the Church Catechism was being drilled into their schoolfellows.

Every Monday morning a strong farm horse took the boys to school; Martin rode in front and held the reins, then a farm lad, Jacob, who had on his arms a big basket filled with brown loaves, boiled bacon and apple turnovers, for the boys took their own food for the week, only asking hot skimmed milk from Friend Lee, who looked after them. Johnnie balanced himself behind Jacob, and over the big Lowfield Heath they trotted, splashing gaily through the pools, as Martin preferred to take a bee-line.

That morning at school, a big lad of thirteen, who was in Martin's class, was looking very dismal. Luke was not a favourite but his little schoolfellow remembered that he had no father and mother, and asked what ailed him.

"It is uncle," said the poor boy. "He says that if I don't get on faster with my schooling he won't pay for a dunderhead, and I shall be 'prenticed at once to a shoemaker—'taint my fault—Mother was so sickly she had to keep me at home to help her and she did want me to be a scholar as Father was. The squire said he would come to school next Saturday and give half-a-crown to the best scholar in each class, and uncle says if I don't get it, with all you chaps so much younger, no more school for me—and I hate the very smell of leather, and Cobbler Jones is drunk half the time," and poor Luke fairly sobbed. Martin looked thoughtful. Lessons were little trouble to him, he was fairly forward in the three Rs for his age, and for geography and for poetry he had a perfect enthusiasm. Half-a-crown would be splendid to take home. Johnnie, in the upper class, with the older lads, had no chance, but Martin might win in the second.

Teacher Sam was quite excited over the old Squire's kind offer, and impressed on the boys that they must work that week and do him credit.

Martin's class was learning "Gray's Elegy." Two verses was the weekly task. They had finished eighteen verses and there were thirteen more.

"Now can't you lads finish it this week to say to Squire? And all the towns in the English counties—you know all but ten of the forty?" he said. "You, little Martin, I'm sure could do it."

Martin said nothing; he looked at Luke's face of dismay, for those were the hardest lessons to him. The practical Bible lesson of last Sunday came home—he would do to Luke as he would wish Luke to do to him were he an orphan boy with a harsh uncle. Luke should win the prize!

When school was over, he drew Luke into a big hollow tree and brought out the paper on which he had laboriously copied the whole of "Gray's Elegy," and, beginning at the nineteenth verse—"Far from the madding crowd's ignoble strife"—he went over the words again and again until Luke's duller memory conquered the difficulties, and also the puzzling geography. Luke, who had never had kindly help with his lessons before, was much cheered and very anxious to succeed.

That night when the brothers went to their bed in the quaint low attic over the Meeting House, Martin lay awake long, watching the moon through the diamond-paned casement. How was he to suppress himself? In teaching Luke he had naturally learned the lesson even more thoroughly than usual. He could not tell Teacher Sam he did not know it! But was it not true that he could not say it? Could not, because it was so much more important that Luke should win the prize.

On Saturday came the old Squire, who kindly questioned the lads, and to Teacher Sam's astonishment, when he called on Martin to recite the "Elegy," the little boy looked down and said, "I'm sorry I can't say it, teacher—but Luke can," and Luke went triumphantly through the long poem and received the coveted half-crown to show his uncle that he was worth more schooling and win exemption from the hated cobbler's stall. Luke was a happy boy that day, but Martin was happier, as on Dobbin's broad back the three splashed through the pools to the farm, where Father and Mother were well content to believe that Martin had done his best, although he never told them *why* he did not bring home the Squire's half-crown.

Maude Robinson

DAVID ALLEN—QUAKER

THE winter that David was nine years old he drove to Cincinnati with his father, in spite of his mother's protests about the cold. When, at the end of a week's jolting behind the six-horse team, they came down the hills into the river city, David was shivering with excitement, and Amos Allen said kindly, "Now I'll stop at the store to trade the bacon and flour for the things I must get. Thee climb out, David, and run down the street to get warm."

David clambered stiffly down. He could not hurry because there were such a number of houses to look at, and so many people to speak to; the country-bred boy could not decently pass any person without saying, "How's thee?" As he stumbled along the walk, round-eyed, a gleeful cry met him.

"Hey, fellers, here's one of them little thee's!"

David looked up to see a crowd of boys unmistakably laughing at him. "Quaker! Quaker!" they sang. David turned back with what dignity he could toward the big covered wagon he had left, now all too far away, and the boys followed, hooting. They must be making fun of his homespun, home-woven, home-cut roundabout, with its straight standing Quaker collar, David thought, self-conscious for the first time; it is not pleasant to discover you are queer. The biggest boy, growing bolder, ran up and aimed a kick at David. Unfortunately for him he missed his mark and sat down hard on the frozen ground; and in the resulting confusion David took to his heels and reached the wagon.

Amos Allen made no comment but he kept David with him the rest of the morning, and in seeing so many strange things, David almost forgot his humiliation. When, wrapped in their warm buffalo robes, they had started homeward again, his father said, "There are many people in Cincinnati now who do not like Friends, David. Most of the city merchants sell goods made by slave labor, because the profit is large, but Friends will not buy from them and urge others not to do so either. That is why I went to Levi Coffin's store; he sells only goods made by free labor, though it is more expensive."

David answered unexpectedly, "I wisht I'd thrown a rock at 'em!" To which his father answered dryly, "I doubt if that would have changed them to thy way of thinking."

That spring Amos Allen bought the eighty acres adjoining his farm to the south, and a colored family, new to the neighborhood, moved into the log cabin that stood on it. Most of the Negro families that David knew were freemen who had moved up from North Carolina to be near the Quaker families who had been their neighbors and protectors in the South. The Johnson family, David's father said, with a warning not to let the story travel farther, were runaway slaves—a grandmother, her son, his wife, and two small children. They had never known any Quakers, but they had steered for a Quaker community because they had heard that Friends could be trusted not to give slaves up to their owners. The grandmother was a valiant old woman, nearly white, who had engineered the venture. When some white men stopped their wagon, thrusting rails between the rickety spokes, and demanded their "free papers," Granny Betsey told them sharply to take the rails out again; these others all belonged to her, she said; she was taking them north to work a farm for her; and the men mistaking her for a white woman apologized and let them go in safety.

David was glad to go with his father to carry a side of bacon to the family one morning. A tall man, stooping to come out through the low cabin door, answered their knock, and thanked them profusely for the bacon. They would not have much to eat besides what he could shoot in the woods till garden time, he said. His manners and words were almost too deferential, the Quaker boy thought, but there was a twinkle in his eye that brought David up short, involuntarily fingering his plain collar. The man was laughing at them.

Amos Allen said quietly, "Thee's welcome to the bacon, Jim. This is my son David. I may send him over with instructions for thee later, if I am too busy to come myself."

Jim Johnson grinned broadly and put out a hand to David. "Well, my little Quaker, thee, thou, though!" he chuckled, as if he thought it were funny. David turned a fiery red and jerked back. It was bad enough to have the dressed-up city boys make fun of him for being a Quaker; but to have this ragged pensioner of his father's charity laughing at him, that was too much.

A deep old voice from the cabin struck in, "Jim, give the little gentleman this here basket," and the man turned good-naturedly to take from a skinny hand, visible in the dim light of the doorway, a basket woven from colored splints. "Granny Betsey, she makes these," he explained.

David made no motion to take the basket held out to him, and his father accepted it for him with thanks. They walked home silently through the sugar-maple woods; and David's mother said it would be a good basket in which to carry her best bonnet to quarterly meeting. That afternoon David said violently that he despised to be a Quaker, and in consequence had to read from *Sewell's Sufferings* for half an hour and drink a cup of hot boneset tea, for fear he was coming down with "fever and aigger"; but even the bitter taste in his mouth could not divert him from his new-found horror of being queer.

He was not a very satisfactory child that summer, though his father had counted on his help. He was not even good at the simple task of carrying messages to the Johnsons' cabin. He knew before he set out that Jim's greeting to him would always be the inane, "Well, my little Quaker, thee, thou, though!" and in consequence he took as much time as he could before meeting Jim, and then often forgot half his message in his fury at being so addressed.

The whole household was unusually restless, and David wasted time when he should have been pulling weeds, wondering why his staid father was taking so many long drives after night. A new phrase, the "Underground Railway," was about; but when David asked what it meant, he was told he was too young to know. Naturally he asked a more promising person, Cousin Elias. Cousin Elias was quite obliging. "The Quakers are taking runaway darkies north," he explained. "Thy father's one of the 'conductors,' and that thicket in the sugar orchard is a 'station,' they say. If they get caught, it's a hundred dollar fine, and half goes to the man that tells. I'd like to have fifty dollars."

"So'd I," said David, thinking of the un-Quakerly clothes fifty dollars would buy. "The Johnsons are runaway slaves," he said incautiously.

Cousin Elias brightened. "Whyn't thee tell somebody? My father doesn't believe in going ag'in the Gover'ment in these things."

"Oh no," said David, thoroughly frightened. "Why, Father—" he could not complete his expression of his father's vast disapproval.

Nevertheless he thought about the Johnsons again. It would serve Jim Johnson right for laughing at him, if he got taken south again. But what about Granny Betsey? When she found that David's mother had taken the first basket, she had made another of even brighter colors for David to keep; it held David's treasures—a round rock, some Indian arrow heads, a piece of yellow keel, some blank paper, and two books. This venture north had been her plan; Jim sometimes grumbled about the cold, and the lack of careless companionship. Granny Betsey said, "You go south and take your lickin's if you want to, Jim. My grandchillen going to be free." But even Jim did not really want to go back.

Amos Allen came in to breakfast with a very serious face one morning. "The Johnsons' owners have traced them," he said. "They may be along here today or tomorrow. Tell the truth about the Johnsons, but tell as little as you can."

David was in a panic. When he saw an unfamiliar horse stop before their house and a dusty man alight from the buggy he retreated to a dim corner, trembling; but his mother at the door seemed perfectly calm. When the buzzing in his ears subsided, David heard the man say, impatiently, "Well, what did these niggahs say about themselves?"

"Friend," said his mother, "I believe the testimony of a Negro slave is not accepted in a court of law; and I do not see, therefore, why I should repeat their words to thee."

To David's immense surprise, the man burst into laughter. "Madam," said he, "you have the best of me. Come on, Bob," he said, "let's go on and not tackle a woman again."

David's esteem for his mother rose with a bound, and was not lowered even by the fact that she quietly fainted as soon as the men were out of sight. He did not know where his father was, but he brought a gourd of water to his mother and she was soon able to drink a little.

"Now, David," she said presently, "take the corn pone from dinner, and the cold potatoes, and the rest of the ham, and put them in thy basket. Put in a little maple sugar, too, and cover it all up well with a towel. Take it down to the thicket in the sugar orchard and thee'll find something to do with it. I can't tell thee any more in case thee should meet some one."

The basket was heavy, but the woods were cool and dim. David went along easily until he had almost reached the thicket, and there he heard loud voices. David crawled hastily back of a blackberry tangle, thankful for his inconspicuous clothing.

A voice he recognized, growled, "Well, we been to the cabin twice and we know they've skipped. That boy said this thicket was the place where they kept the niggahs, but we can't find the path. Let's shoot into it a time or two, and then wait."

The gun fired, not once but half a dozen times, but there was no answer. "Now we'll wait," said the voice grimly. They settled themselves quite near David, who crouched uncomfortably while the minutes went slowly by. The sun was nearly down, when the voice said, "No use waiting. We'll have to take to the road again if we find them."

David's legs were stiff and the obscure little path into the thicket was hard to follow, but something bigger than himself sent him pushing on with his basket. In a clear spot in the center of the tangle he found the Johnsons, as he had expected. Granny Betsey had a bandaged arm where a shot had struck her, but she was still the bravest of all of them.

"Good-by, David," she said, "I reckon I won't see you

again; but I won't never forget you Quaker folks. You're real human folks, like God meant folks to be."

David escaped in a wordless embarrassment that was somehow pleasant. That night his father was away again on a long drive, and though the Johnsons were not mentioned, David knew that he would not see them again at the cabin or in the thicket.

It was weeks before he told his father of his adventure in the woods, and then Amos Allen said, "Yes, Betsey Johnson told me the story just about as thee has. She thought thee was a pretty good Quaker, David, and so do I!"

"Oh!" exclaimed David, in surprised relief, "Is that what Jim meant when he called me a Quaker?"

Marjorie Hill Allee

THE SACRED FLAME

Long, long ago, in the days of brave knights and lovely ladies, men fought on horseback with sword and lance, and adventure seemed the busines of life. In those far days, inspired by the teaching and preaching of earnest monks, was begun that wonderful series of pilgrimages to the Holy City of Jerusalem, called the Crusades.

Many brave knights traveled the weary miles with their trains of trusty followers. They forded deep rivers, climbed great mountains, and crossed the burning desert sands to rescue from the infidel Turks the tomb of Jesus.

But it was a cruel age and many of the knights were cruel, self-seeking men who pillaged, burned, and killed even while bent on so high an errand.

In one of the great churches of the beautiful city of Florence, in Italy, were gathered on a spring evening a company of knights, brave men all. They were clad in shining armor, with clanking swords and bright pennants, and had come for the blessing and benediction of the priests before starting on their crusade on the morrow. Among this company was Raniero de Raniero, a gallant figure and one whose beauty and fine bearing all must admire, but whose heart was cruel and selfish. He was feared and hated by those nearest him and he thought only of his own advancement and gain. Even his beautiful wife Francesca was perhaps secretly glad to see him start on this journey, for to her he was not loving, but heartless and unkind.

Raniero knelt before the altar and vowed, not a secret vow in his heart, but so that all men might know and admire, to bring back to Florence from Jerusalem the most precious thing that he should find.

The Turks were rich in gold and jewels, and to the minds of all present came a picture of the glittering treasure which Raniero would bring to their church.

So on the morrow they started, amid the acclaim and applause of the citizens, and none rode his horse so straight or held his head so high as Raniero de Raniero. The way was long and hard, and many and bitter were the battles fought before even the land of Palestine was reached, but in all Raniero kept in the forefront of the fight and proved himself an intrepid warrior.

When at last they reached Jerusalem and laid siege to the city, Raniero was second only to Godfrey of Boulogne, the leader, in deeds of prowess. On the night following their triumphant entry, all the proud knights, dressed in the long dark robes of penitents and with bare feet, marched through the silent city streets to the church of the Holy Sepulchre, each carrying an unlighted candle in his hand.

To Raniero, as a reward for his prowess, had been given the privilege of being first to light his taper from the flame that burned before the sacred tomb of Christ. There was no clank of armor, only the soft footfalls of this company of knights—penitent in garb but, oh! so many proud and hard of heart—and Raniero, at their head, pacing up the dark aisle toward the sacred flame.

Suddenly to Raniero all the light of the world seemed to glow within that point of light, and he felt himself moving toward it through endless darkness and desiring it more than he had ever wanted anything before; and as he knelt and reached his little taper toward the flame he felt that he was about to achieve the most precious thing in the world. In the hush of that strange service came to Raniero the conviction that this was the gift which he had vowed to carry back to Florence.

In the morning Raniero announced to his followers that he was about to start for home and bear his sacred gift.

Loud and long they laughed! Why, the booty captured from the Turks was still to be divided—turn their backs on that? No, indeed! There was still gallant adventure and much of pleasure. If he would start on such a fool's errand he must go alone! To carry a lighted candle from Jerusalem to Florence was an impossible feat, even without the dangers and hardships of the way.

Raniero heeded neither their jeers and laughter nor their advice and warning. The next morning, clad in armor, over which he had thrown a heavy cloak, with sword and battle-axe, and a great bundle of extra tapers to feed his flame, he started on the homeward pilgrimage with the burning candle in his hand.

He called a gay farewell to the amazed group gathered to watch his departure and galloped off. Very quickly he realized that he could not go very swiftly—the little light wavered and he must need draw his horse to a walk that it might flare up again. "How strange," he said, "that this light when almost gone, will shine again in the stillness!"

One day when passing through a wild and lonely defile, he saw before him a company of rough men, clearly one of the robber bands with which the lawless country was infested. They were few and poorly armed and his first thought was to gallop through them, striking right and left with his huge sword, but no—the little light was far too frail for such a venture, and proud Raniero rode slowly into the midst of the robber band and said, "Friends, take what you will, but do not harm my light."

Amazed, they followed his suggestion and took horse, money, armor, sword—naught was left him but the heavy coat and the burning taper. On leaving, the leader of the band, touched perhaps by his sad plight, called, "Take my

horse, 'tis fast enough to carry a candle!"—and with mocking laughs they rode away.

So Raniero on the raw-boned old steed traveled the
weary miles—resting when the wind was fresh and pressing on when the sun burned clear—for so the light throve
best. Raniero, who always had thought first of his own
comfort, now gauged his actions by the little twinkling
flame.

Once on a lonely mountain path a woman ran from a
little cottage calling, "Stranger, give me, I pray you, a light
from your candle! My fire has gone out and I can bake no
bread for my children."

"No, no," said Raniero, "the light I carry is too sacred for
common use. I cannot give you."

But the woman pled with him, saying, "The light I
would guard is my children's lives—it will not lessen your
flame to give to me."

So Raniero listened to her pleading and lighted her lamp
and it seemed to him that his flame burned more brightly.

In the night on the mountains came suddenly a terrible
storm of wind, and rain and hail. Though Raniero struggled valiantly and was himself soaked by the rain and
bruised and buffeted by wind and hail, the little flame
went out! Utterly discouraged he sank upon the wet
ground, incentive gone, a hopeless blank before him. Suddenly he sprang up, "The woman's light is the sacred
flame!" he cried. "By giving I have saved it!" and he started
at once in the dark and went down the mountain path to
the cottage.

When he reached the little cottage, he saw the flicker
of fire on the hearth, and he knew that it was the sacred
flame which he had given the mother only a few hours
before.

In the morning sun he started on again. The light

burned brightly, the way seemed green and pleasant and the little birds sang.

Soon he met a party of knights who, seeing him guarding so carefully a lighted candle, called, "A mad man! surely a mad man!"

But their leader, one Robert Taillifer, bid them be silent and asked, "Have you traveled far so, my friend?"

"All the way from Jerusalem," answered Raniero.

"And how often has the light gone out?" he asked.

And Raniero answered, "Still burns the flame with which I rode from the Holy City."

Then Robert Taillifer bowed his head.

"I, too, am one who guards a sacred flame," he said. "Tell me, I beg thee, thou who hast kept thy light burning so long—what must I do to keep mine shining always?"

"Master, it is a difficult task, though it seemed so easy at first. This must thou do to keep the flame—thou must mind the light continually."

And Robert Taillifer smiled and answered, "What thou hast done for thy sacred flame I may do for mine!"

As Raniero de Raniero rode nearer and nearer to home his thoughts went back to Palestine and to his comrades fighting there, but he felt no thrill at the thought of many trophies or the call to arms. The quiet of the Italian hills and the golden sunshine filled him with a mighty peace as he looked at his candle burning brightly. "Surely this light hath recreated me!" he said.

As he came to the outskirts of Florence the inhabitants marvelled at the handsome, weather-beaten man on the gaunt, old horse. He was ragged and tattered and carried a lighted candle. A crowd followed him, growing larger, as crowds will, and from laughter and wonder, changing to jeers, threats, and open hostility.

"Put out his light! Put out his light!" called the people,

throwing stones and reaching for the candle. Raniero, desperate, struggled on. Would no one recognize the gallant knight who had ridden forth so bravely from these same streets? He held the light high, searching the jeering faces before him for some understanding response.

Suddenly from a balcony above him a woman leaned over and snatched the burning candle, and the crowd, shrieking with laughter, hooted afresh.

Poor Raniero swayed in his saddle and fell to the street unconscious. The cruel crowd surged away in search of further excitement and the old horse stood in the deserted street by the side of the ragged man.

As Raniero wearily opened his eyes he saw, bending over him, his wife, Francesca, who of all the multitude had recognized him.

"I took the light," she said; "I am guarding it." So understanding love had once again saved the flame.

Together they took the candle to the church and Raniero recounted to the priest the tale of his long pilgrimage and had the joy of placing on the altar the little light he had grown so much to love.

After the service the priest said to the gathered people: "This is the flame, taken from the sacred tomb of our Lord in Jerusalem, which Raniero de Raniero has carried all the long miles to Florence. The most precious thing he found!"

And the people remembering the proud and cruel Raniero doubted and could not believe.

"How do we know?" they asked.

The priest beckoned to Raniero, who stepped forward and took from the altar the light he had tended so long. His whole being focussed in its brightness, he felt that the people must believe in his gift, that it could not be possible they should doubt so mighty a certainty, and as he stood before them, holding the precious flame, a wonderful thing happened.

In his face came a radiant light, reflecting and increasing the little light he held, till the dim chancel grew luminous, and the people fell upon their knees, exclaiming, "It is the Light! It is the Light! He carries it in his face!"

And the priest with bowed head said, "God grant we may keep the Sacred Flame burning in Florence!"

Adapted from Christ Legends, *by Selma Lagerlöf. Used by permission of Henry Holt & Company.*

THE SILVER TANKARD
TTTTTTTTTTTTTTTTTTTTTTTTTTTTTTTTTTTTTTTTTTTTT

DANIEL GORDON whistled as he backed Jerry into the buggy shafts and rapidly buckled the harness. It was Sunday morning and he and his wife would be late to meeting if they weren't off soon. The two boys had started on the ten-mile ride a half-hour ago—but Jerry would soon overtake Dobbin, loaded as he was with the two of them on his back. Little Hetty would stay at home today. She did not mind being left alone and the long drive tired her. She was only nine—too much must not be expected of the dear child.

Daniel's train of thought was broken by the sudden appearance of John Perkins around the corner of the barn. Daniel stared at Perkins in astonishment, for though he was his nearest neighbor, six miles of rough Maine wilderness lay between their fertile valley farms. Perkins should be on his way to meeting now, instead of calling on his friends. Daniel's cheery questions were interrupted by Perkins, who spoke quickly, with a solemn face. "I don't think it safe for you all to go to meeting today, Daniel."

"What's amiss, John? The boys are already off; wife and I are just leaving. Hetty will be here."

"Hetty mustn't be left alone. Listen, Daniel! Tom Smith and his two men have been seen in the wood by Crooked Fork. They know of your old silver tankard and plates, and Tom is reported to have sworn when drunk to get them from you before the summer passes. You know what that means."

Daniel knew only too well. Tom Smith and his gang were desperate men who lived by swooping down upon first one lonely farmhouse and then another, seizing by force whatever was valuable in the house, and then disappearing beyond the reach of the law. In this thinly settled country a hundred years ago a police force was unknown, and land pirates such as these had their own way. Everyone in this part of Maine knew of the Gordon tankard and plates, brought from England years before. Tom Smith had sworn to get them—and he always kept his word in such matters.

Daniel stood in deep thought. His religious faith was very simple and profoundly deep. He believed with his whole soul that God would take care of those who did their duty and put their trust absolutely in Him. He had tried all his life to live in this faith. Here was indeed a severe test. The thieves might not come; neighbor Perkins might be mistaken; still the risk in leaving his little Hetty alone was great. Yet he would do it. His duty plainly was to go to meeting. To take her with him would be to teach her fear. He would place her in God's hands, and trust.

"Hetty," said Daniel as he kissed her rather more solemnly than usual, and climbed into the buggy beside his wife, "if any strangers come while we are gone, treat them well. We can spare of our abundance to feed the poor. What is gold and silver compared to God's words of love?" Hetty was puzzled to see her father's face so troubled.

After making the kitchen tidy, Hetty sat down by the window with a book. It was very quiet and she felt a little lonely. Only an hour had passed and the family would be away for a long time yet. She looked out of the window and was overjoyed to see three men walking rapidly up the road toward the house. Her father must have been expecting them, she thought. That was why he spoke about treating strangers well. She ran down the path to meet them, courtesied politely, and cried eagerly:

"Won't you please come in? Father will be so sorry not

to see you, but he bade me serve you in any way I could."

"Are you alone here?" eagerly asked the youngest man, who was Tom Smith.

"Oh, yes, I am quite alone. If Mother were here she would do more for you, but I'll do all I can."

The men stared at each other in silence, and entered the neat, comfortable kitchen. The silver tankard stood on the huge old sideboard, and behind it a row of silver plates. The men hesitated a moment—then the oldest one stepped toward the sideboard.

"You're going to be seated and allow me to prepare a meal for you, are you not?" said Hetty, in a panic lest her guests would not feel at home and leave her alone again all too soon.

Smith dropped into a chair as though his knees had suddenly given way under him. "Yes, we will, thank you, my child, for we are all hungry," he replied in a voice that sounded to Hetty only rather husky, but made his companions turn and stare in astonishment.

For several minutes Hetty flitted in and out, while the men watched in silence. She dragged forward the table that stood against the wall, and Smith sprang forward to help her. While he was doing this she asked him to kindly lift down the tankard and three of the best silver plates. Cold cider she brought from the cellar and filled the tankard to the brim, butter from the springhouse, a huge loaf of bread. She paused a moment, her little forehead wrinkled in perplexity.

"Would you prefer to have some cold roast pork right away, or wait while I cook one of Mother's chickens?"

"We can't wait. Give us what you have," muttered one of the older men, his eyes fixed on the food.

Soon all was ready, and with another gay little bow Hetty invited her guests to be seated. As she watched them eat she thought she had never in her life seen such strange manners. They seized the meat in their fingers and gulped it down ravenously as though they had not tasted food for days, which was indeed about the case. First one and then another took long drinks from the silver tankard until it was quite empty and Hetty hurried to fill it again. All the while no word was spoken and the men seemed to avoid looking in her direction.

Finally, when the table was almost bare and they had shaken their heads at all her offers of more bread or meat, Smith started from his chair with a sudden, "Come, let's go."

Hetty was surprised at his lack of politeness, and more amazed when the older man replied, "What, go with empty hands with all this silver here?" and he seized the tankard.

For the first time Hetty felt a chill of fear. "Oh, please," she cried, "it is my father's."

Smith leaned across and clutched the man roughly by the arm. "Put that down," he shouted. "I'll shoot the man who takes a single thing from this house."

Hetty looked in terror from one to the other as they stood glaring across the table, then she ran to Smith's side and pressed close against his arm as the other men turned and walked sullenly out of the house, muttering to themselves. Smith looked down at Hetty's trusting little upturned face, and a strange softness came into his eyes. He turned abruptly after the others, and Hetty, very much puzzled, watched the three men stalk down the road and out of sight.

When Daniel and his wife drove in that afternoon an hour earlier than usual, the horse covered with lather, Hetty greeted them with:

"Your strangers came, Father, and I treated them well, but they forgot to thank me."

MY GREAT-UNCLE

I who tell you this story am a very old man now. I have long possessed and read "The Memoirs of Daniel Wheeler" and I have a profound respect for his labors as a Quaker missionary and preacher. But this reverend figure is not *my* great-uncle, the romantic hero who lit up my drab and creeping childhood, set me on a level with my fellow-men and poured red courage into my anaemic veins.

In the year 1849 when I was barely nine years old I was sent to a Quaker boarding school in Oxfordshire. My mother, being poor, had asked her well-to-do relations to help with her children's education, and they had decreed that I was to go to Sibford School.

I was a small, shy, sensitive scrap of a boy, lonely and homesick, and frightened by the teasing of the other boys. All of them seemed to have friends or relations who came to see them. I had none. I knew I had lots of relations somewhere, but I thought of them all as important, highly religious people, who could have no interest in a small boy like me.

I comforted myself by day-dreaming, wonderful dreams in which I was always a hero admired by all the boys for my exploits. But in actual life I was shrinking and tearful, creeping about in the background.

I wonder whether my poor little self would ever have learnt self-confidence and courage, ever have faced up to life and to people and found a place in the world, had it not been for my Great-Uncle.

It happened this way.

One day when I was ten the door of my class-room opened and the Head Master stalked in followed by a burly, bearded, middle-aged man. Instead of bringing his guest in, the Head Master looked round, caught my eye and said, "I want thee Michael." I started up guiltily, and the next minute found the Head Master introducing me to the bearded man.

"This is the boy," he said. "Daniel Wheeler was his mother's uncle." Then he turned back to speak to the class-master and left us together.

The stranger seized on my hand, shook it up and down rapturously while he beamed on me. He spoke with a rough nasal voice which I afterwards learnt was due to his living much in America.

"Well, well," he said. "To think that Daniel Wheeler was your great-uncle. This is an honor," he continued and pump-handled my arm even more vigorously. "How old are you, Sonnie?"

I told him I was born in June 1840.

"That's a pity, the very month he died. Ah! he was a great man. I was the Captain of his ship, you know."

I started. I had heard vague occasional talk of an aged uncle, a great Light in the Society of Friends, just another of those far-removed official relations, a dead one in this case. But the owner of a ship! That was different!

"Captain of his ship!" I repeated in my astonishment.

"Yes, 'The Henry Freeling' was her name. Thousands of miles I've sailed in her with him aboard, and time upon time I thought we'd founder in her together. Such storms! You'd have thought your uncle was a Jonah instead of the best and bravest of men. Brave! There he'd be, not a dry inch on the ship, bitter cold, great seas sweeping over the decks, sailors lashed to spars to keep 'em from going overboard, all of us expecting every minute to be our last, and there he'd be, calm as you make 'em—more like than not reading his Bible to us!"

"But was the ship all his?" I asked, when he paused.

"Well, if she weren't exactly his, she was all for him to sail off to the South Sea Islands in."

"Were there cannibals?" I asked wide-eyed.

"Cannibals they'd been a few years back," he said.

"Cannibals!"

For the first time in my life I was talking fearlessly to a stranger, my wretched little self quite forgotten. But at that point the Head Master came back, and the Captain, realizing the interview was over, began pump-handling again.

"Very pleased to have met you, young 'un. You grow up to be like your great-uncle. You can't do better." And he slipped sixpence—a prodigious sum—into my hand.

Dazed and bewildered I went back to my classmates.

"Who was the Johnny?" asked one casually when work was over.

"The Captain of my uncle's ship," I said with a beating heart. I had my moment. They all paused. I continued:

"My uncle was great. He was brave as a lion. He went among cannibals. He was nearly drowned many times."

"Who's been stuffing you?" said one.

"You never said you had an uncle who owned a ship!" said another.

"You're making it up, Mike," said a third.

"I'm not, I'm not," I protested. "The Captain said my uncle was great, he kept on saying it, and he said he was honored to meet me."

This was too much for them. They broke into shouts of laughter, and my triumph was turned into shame and confusion. They pretended to shake my hand reverently and thank me effusively for letting them do it. They made such game of me that I retired to the washroom in tears.

But I believed in my Captain. This time I was not

beaten to the dust. If only I could see him again! "I must," I said frantically to myself. "I must, I must." Urgency set my small brain working. I remembered that visitors often stayed in a house opposite the school, and with a new desperate kind of courage I slipped out next morning in the ten minutes' recess, knocked at the front-door and stammeringly asked if "the Captain" was there.

"No," said a servant girl who came to the door, and was about to shut it on me, when, perhaps seeing the despair in my face, she added, "There's a man with a sea-hat on staying at Sarah Lamb's."

"Sarah Lamb's" was half a mile away. I broke bounds again after dinner. I was in a state to break anything. Happily for me I met him along the road.

"Hello," he said, "going for a paper-chase?"

"No, no," I panted, for I had run all the way, "I must go back or they'll catch me." Then with a rush it came. "The boys won't believe what you said about my having an uncle who was great."

I did right to trust that man. He divined at once that something terribly important to me was at stake, my little ship was in peril and this expert in storms did not waste time over explanations. He set to work.

"Your friends can't come here. Sarah Lamb's my wife's cousin, but . . ." he broke off. "Let me see. I thought of attending your Quaker Meeting on Sunday, just in his memory. I'm no Quaker myself. It's held near the School, I hear." I nodded. "Now have you boys any free time after the Meeting?"

I answered him that we could go anywhere we liked on school ground for an hour afterwards. We settled things, and then he added:

"You tell them friends of yours there'll be gingerbreads for all." What a plotter he was! Gingerbreads would bring them. Wildly excited I ran back and slipped into class unnoticed.

Sunday came at last. Would that meeting never end? My Captain was seated near the door and we exchanged glances as I marched out in file. Outside he slipped an arm in mine, and we sauntered nonchalantly out of the garden gate, along the school paddock, to a place behind a barn, boys' heads popping up as we went. The field had been newly-mown, I remember, and it was a warm day. We sat down with our backs to an old hay rick, and ginger-breads were generously distributed.

The Captain began. He was a born story-teller and Homer himself could not have held an audience more spell-bound. The sharp straws stuck unheeded down the necks of our First-day suits, and gingerbreads grew sodden in our hot palms. He told us of my uncle's long voyage in "The Henry Freeling"; of terrible storms round the Cape of Good Hope; of the Island of Tristian D'Acuna, 1500 miles off any other land; of bitter frost; and of a miraculous visitation of 200 whales who swam round the ship acting as a break-water to otherwise all-engulfing billows.

I can still recall the thrill of satisfaction that ran down my spine when he told us how they had been chased by pirates and how, often, "The Henry Freeling," itself, had been mistaken for a pirate ship.

"And cannibals," I reminded him, as he at last paused.

Then we heard about landings on South Sea Islands, of native queens, of ceremonies and alarms, of the honor given to my uncle by local missionaries.

And as a last and wonderful thrill, just before we broke up, summoned by the first-bell, the Captain shook my hand warmly, and said, "Young man, you ought to get someone to tell you about your great-uncle's doings in Russia before he came a-voyaging with me."

"In Russia!" I gasped, feeling that there was no end to this greatest of uncles.

"Yes, Russia. Of course I've only heard about it at second hand. I've been told that he was specially invited out there by Alexander the Great—you know, the Emperor of all the Russians. And the Emperor and Empress used to visit him, and he lived in a castle near St. Petersburg, and wolves used to come round it in the winter and bite his servants so that they went raving mad."

I found out later that legend had already begun to color this account of my uncle's life in Russia. But by this time we boys were ready to believe anything. Castles infested by wolves fitted in easily, and why should not an Alexander the Great hobnob with an Uncle the Great?

I had no more trouble with the disbelief of my school-mates. One or two doubting Thomases consulted their parents, but they learnt that Daniel Wheeler had indeed existed, and if their informers tried to change the emphasis from bold buccaneer to weighty Friend and preacher, we boys knew better, for we had heard the story direct. The Captain went back to his ship that Sunday evening and I have never heard of him since. But my gratitude to him has been undying. He gave me my Great-Uncle, he let me know that I had a hero's blood in my veins. No longer could I be shrinking and afraid. In a few months I had changed into a noisy, assertive, rather lawless school-boy, constantly getting into scrapes. Whenever I lacked courage or endurance, I had only to say to myself "my Great-Uncle" and power grew in me.

Abridged from the story in the Friends Quarterly, October 1948 by Caroline C. Graveson, a great-niece of Daniel Wheeler and the daughter of the old man who tells the story.

FAINT HEART FAILED

Two brothers were talking earnestly in the candlelight of a one room log cabin. Dressed alike in the plain garb of the Society of Friends and with a strong family resemblance, they nevertheless presented a marked contrast. Miles, though only a little older than Henry, showed the results of a pioneer's struggle for existence. His face bore lines of care and anxiety and his shoulders drooped slightly. Restlessness mingled with grim determination in his demeanor.

Henry, no less determined, had still retained the thrill of adventure with which he had set out from England many months ago to seek freedom in a new world.

"We must rise before light tomorrow," Miles was saying, "and go to the upland clearing. Our corn is certainly ready for its first hoeing. That was splendid seed old Arrow-in-the-Dark gave thee."

"A fine stand of corn, Miles, and the rain last week came just right for it. But there's a long day's work ahead. Shall we take our dinner with us? We can eat it under the pines by the brook."

"Ay, that is well-planned. As the crow flies, it cannot be more than two miles from here, but the way we poor mortals must travel seems a journey indeed. It's a lonely spot. From the bare knoll to the west, one faces a whole new world. Thou know'st the place I mean, Henry?"

"Indian Rock? Ay, 'tis there the braves hold their War Council. Night before last they met, some say an hundred strong, all in war paint and feathers. The village has posted sentries. This morning men were at work strengthening the stockade, and bringing in supplies to stand a siege, if necessary. I would that they might see their mistake in

183

season. Fear breeds fear. If the settlers shared our conviction against violence, the Indians would trust them, as they trust us."

"Thy faith never falters, does it, Henry?"

"Why should it falter? Our dealings with the savages have been acts of friendship, and in return they have given assistance and helpful advice. Arrow-in-the-Dark told me about planting corn on the ridge above the frost, and what time of the moon to plant, after the oak buds opened."

Miles shook his head solemnly and cast a glance toward the open doorway before he replied in a low voice, "Thomas Vinton cautioned me only yesterday against our going to work in the upland unarmed. He said that Arrow-in-the-Dark was old in craft, and his giving us that plot of ground so far from the village was but setting a trap for us. 'Next full moon your scalps may be dangling from Arrow-in-the-Dark's belt and squaws will take over a corn patch planted and hoed by two white men whose bones the crows are picking. Better go armed,' counselled Thomas."

"Cheerful advice, that. I don't believe a word of it. Arrow-in-the-Dark is a man of honor. I'd trust him as I'd trust thee, Miles."

Before daylight the next morning the two brothers set out, carrying in a light basket of birchbark enough simple food for their dinner. For drink they counted only on the sparkling brook-water, and Henry hoped to find the sunny slope to the south of Indian Rock red with wild strawberries. Arrow-in-the-Dark had showed him the white blossoms.

"The Great Spirit," the old Chief had told him, "causes the fruit to ripen, a gift to all his children without toil or payment. The Indian shows his White Brother where to look for them. Take what you wish. There is peace between us."

At noon, after a hard morning's hoeing, Miles and Henry sat down by the brook to eat, rested a bit, and then went to see whether the wild strawberries were ripening. They found the berries just commencing to crimson beneath the green leaves.

"In another week there will be quantities. Dost thou not find their taste delicious, Miles?"

Henry had been clambering up the steep face of Indian Rock. Miles watched him, but stayed below, still hunting for berries, and rather soberly wondering if they were not being watched by ambushed Indians.

During the afternoon Miles was absorbed, and they hoed silently, side by side, anxious to finish the last rows before sunset. But hard as they toiled, they presently saw that they must return in the morning.

On their way home they heard rustling in the hazel brush along the trail, and the eerie cry of the whip-poor-will across the dusk of the lowland.

"The Indians can imitate every bird and every wild creature of the forest. One never knows whether what one hears is the true or the false. But methinks never were whip-poor-wills so plentiful as this evening. Birds, they may be, but more likely signals as the village is being surrounded by savages."

"Miles, prithee frighten not thyself nor me by thy talk. If the Indians rise against us, they rise. But to my thinking, a show of resistance on the part of the village will cause them to rise all the sooner."

At the edge of the settlement an armed party of villagers came out to meet the brothers.

"Thank God, friends, ye be safe returned! Bad news arrived by messenger within the hour. A half score leagues to the eastward the savages are on the war-path. Many of those settlers have been massacred, for they were unwarned. We have word in season. Tonight all gather within the stockade. 'Tis our only security. Though we be but a handful, every man is well-armed, and every man will be needed for defense."

"I do not fear the Indians," said Henry stoutly. "Arrow-in-the-Dark has ever been friendly. If *we* arm, *they* arm. Nor can we blame a savage if he take a leaf from our book."

"Well enough to practice peace in peace times, neighbor. War is a grim fact. There are our women and children to think of."

"I do think of them," replied Henry. "Their chances are far better without resistance on your part."

The armed villagers laughed aloud at Henry's simple-mindedness.

"What would be your defense, then?"

"To proceed as usual. Miles and I ever sleep in our cabin with the latch-string out. Tomorrow we go back to finish hoeing our corn patch. And a fine stand of corn we have. If it harvests well, there will be plenty for us all, man, woman, and child."

"Do you hoe under the shadow of Indian Rock without arms?" sneered a voice.

"Assuredly. Why should we not?"

"You'll never live to see your corn in tassel. Braves on the war-path spare none. The more scalps, the more glory."

That evening the brothers talked again in the darkness, and the fear which prevailed in the village kept them alert for sounds of danger. But no harm came during the night, and at dawn they made ready for work again.

"We can finish ere noon, methinks," said Miles. "No need to carry food with us. But hark thee, Henry. I lay till long after midnight, pondering on our situation. It may be sheer foolhardiness and bravado to go to a lonely place unarmed. When we go to the forest for game we carry muskets. Today if we take along powderhorns and muskets the Indians will see that we are armed and fear to attack us. I would never shoot a man, red or white, being, as thou knowest, a stout believer in peace. But just bearing a weapon may serve to keep the warriors at a distance. In sooth, Henry, I like my scalp where Nature put it, as well as any man. So I go forth this morning, hoe on one shoulder, and musket on t'other. And so I intend to return, the hoe having performed an active service, and the musket a passive one."

"I think thee wrong, Miles. The Indians will conclude that we no longer trust in their good faith. Arrow-in-the-Dark is our friend."

"These hostile Indians may be none of his tribe. Nay, Henry, I am older than thou. Be guided by my counsel. 'Tis folly to throw our lives away. Our strength and our usefulness we owe to the community."

So in the fair, pink sunrise the two brothers set out to hoe their Indian corn. In silhouette against the morning sky their tall figures strode on, Henry with a hoe, and Miles ahead with a musket over one shoulder and a hoe over the other. The younger man was sullen and sick at heart. The elder was a prey to fears unknown to him when he believed in good faith between Indians and settlers. He was a little ashamed of his defection, and felt that he had fallen in Henry's estimation. They went on in silent discomfort, unhappy at not being in their customary accord.

The path they took skirted the knoll called Indian Rock. Suddenly from behind thickets of hazel and alder came a rain of arrows. Miles was struck, and then Henry. Side by side they lay, not a hundred yards from their growing corn. They lay still, mercifully pierced to the heart by the sure aim of the warriors.

Later in the day came Arrow-in-the-Dark to the corn field to see if the brothers were safe. He found them lying scalped in the path.

"Those were my friends you have slain," he said sternly to his tribesmen.

"Friends do not bring muskets when they work in the fields, O Chief!" replied the warriors. "They came against our Council Rock with a musket. Behold beside their bodies, the musket loaded to kill. So we killed first. Yesterday we watched also. They brought only hoes, and food. They ate berries and drank water. We let them live. Today they are dead. Peace had gone from their hearts."

THE HIGHWAYMAN

THE perfect serenity of a star-lit April night was broken by the chorus of piping frogs from a little valley. The road, winding down an abrupt hillside, lost itself in the shadow of a tangled grove and reappeared beside the stretch of marsh grass in which the peepers made merry. Now and then came the chiding "boom" of an old bullfrog, like a teacher reminding the children that this was a solemn occasion, but the impudent youngsters paid no attention.

To the man crouched behind the alder bushes the tranquility of the night seemed to mock the storm within himself. Up the hill, still out of sight, his straining ears caught the sound of a horse's hoof clattering among the loose stones of the hard dirt road. As he listened, a gust of horror at the thing he was about to do shook him and the throbbing of his heart stifled him. But he kept his eyes steadily upon the little stretch of white road that the horse and rider must pass before they entered the deep shadow of the trees beside him.

Although many times before the highwayman had thus lain in wait for some unsuspecting traveller, he never ceased to hate this means of snatching a living from the world. While a young man, with good prospects as a skilful carpenter, he had been unjustly accused of stealing a bag of money from the boss's carriage and was condemned to a year's imprisonment. With prison behind him, bitter and proud, he had tried to pick up his old trade, only to find that no one would give him employment. He tried desperately to win the confidence and friendship which he coveted, only to be met with suspicion. Finally he gave up the struggle and determined to live up to his bad reputation.

Around the bend, the horse picking his way carefully, came his victim. The glow of the stars shone upon his slightly upturned face, and the highwayman noted with the eye of an expert that the rider was about middle height, strong and thick-set, with a firm seat that would be hard to upset, and long muscular arms that could doubtless deal mighty blows. It was a point of pride with the highwayman never to allow the apparent strength of his opponent to take away his nerve, and he immediately became perfectly calm as the rider entered the shadow and clattered across the loose planks of a tiny bridge.

Two quick strides and the highwayman was at the horse's head, had seized the rein, and though the horse leaped to one side, rearing and jerking its head violently, he clung grimly, shielding his head with his left arm from the expected blow from above.

"Steady—Bess—steady!" commanded the rider, and the horse stood trembling.

The highwayman whipped out a pistol, crying fiercely, "Your purse, or I shoot!"

To his amazement a calm voice replied, "If thou wouldst not pull her mouth she would stand more quietly. Her mouth has always been most sensitive."

The highwayman thought rapidly—a trick to gain time—the man is armed—unfrightened—and will resist desperately. He ducked his head under the horse's neck and the animal started nervously.

"Whoa, Bess! Hush, girl! Here is my purse containing all that I have with me, except a one-pound note in the near saddle-bag. A neighbor's wife gave that to me with samples of the calico I am to buy her."

The highwayman braced himself, for the gesture of that

strong arm above must certainly mean resistance. But the hand only held a fat leather wallet and he loosed the reins to snatch it. As he did so the horse's shoulder knocked the pistol from his hand.

"Get off your horse or I'll shoot it from under you!" the highwayman cried, leaping to the side of the road as the horse pranced on the spot where the weapon lay. "On the instant, I tell you!"

The rider pulled down his horse, sat motionless for a breathless moment, then swung himself down slowly, without a word. The robber darted forward, leaped into the saddle and jerked the horse about to make his escape before his uncanny victim should open fire. A hand on the reins stopped him, and to his amazement the man said:

"I have given thee what thou asked for, but thou wilt have to render an account of it before God. By the holy Light that shines within each one of us, how dost thou dare thus to ignore thy Master's voice, pleading with thee to turn aside from the paths of evil to follow him?"

The tension broke as the highwayman realized with anger that the man, instead of resisting, was preaching to him. All the bitterness of his life spoke in his snarl, "Loose the reins and hold your tongue, or I'll blow your brains out!"

"Nay, friend, thy weapon lies in the dirt. But though I would not give my life for my money or my horse, I would give it to save thy soul."

The highwayman was struck by a new and almost unbelievable thought. This man knew before he dismounted that the pistol had fallen; he had every advantage with which to either strike or flee, and yet he had quietly given what was asked with no sign of fear—indeed he spoke almost with gentleness. Could it be that God, of whom the highwayman had not thought for years, was speaking to him? In a swift panic he leaped from the horse, pressed the wallet with a hurried "Take it, take it!" into the good man's hands. Turning, he plunged down the road, but as he ran he heard, "Mayst thou receive guidance from above, and if I, Leonard Fell, can do aught to aid thee—" He ran on, but despair had left him. He became suddenly aware of a strange stirring in his soul that somehow seemed in harmony with the beauty of the night.

THE INVINCIBLE LEADER

"Tell me a story about when you were a great soldier. Tell me about one of the battles you won," said a little boy to his grandfather.

The old man had been a colonel in the Austrian army for many years and could recount fierce tales of conquest by his troops. But today he shook his head as he took the boy upon his knee.

"I will tell you, instead," he said, "of the greatest battle I ever lost, which was won by braver men than mine."

The little boy was astonished, for he thought that his grandfather's soldiers were the bravest in the world. So he listened eagerly.

"I was commanded," the old colonel began, "to march against a little town in the Tyrol and lay siege to it. We had been meeting stubborn resistance in that part of the country, but we felt sure that we should win because all of the advantages were on our side. My confidence, however, was arrested by a remark from a prisoner we had taken. 'You will never take that town,' he said, 'for they have an Invincible Leader.'

" 'What does the fellow mean?' I inquired of one of my staff. 'And who is this leader of whom he speaks?'

"Nobody seemed able to answer my question, and so in case there should be some truth in the report, I doubled preparations.

"As we descended through the pass in the Alps, I saw with surprise that the cattle were still grazing in the valley and that women and children—yes, and even men—were working in the fields.

" 'Either they are not expecting us, or this is a trap to

catch us,' I thought to myself. As we drew nearer the town we passed people on the road. They smiled and greeted us with a friendly word, and then went on their way. So friendly was their attitude toward us, and so different from the usual reception given us, that my soldiers forgot they were under discipline and returned the greeting.

"Finally we reached the town and clattered up the cobble-paved streets—colors flying, horns sounding a challenge, arms in readiness. The forge of the blacksmith shop was glowing, and the smith left it to stand in the door with a number of others to watch us pass. Suddenly he waved to one of my soldiers and I heard him exclaim, 'I knew that fellow when we were boys together at Innsbruch!'

"Women came to the windows or doorways with little babies in their arms. Some of them looked startled and held the babies closer, then went quietly on with their household tasks without panic or confusion. As for the boys—little fellows like you, my son," the old man cuddled the boy in his arms; "they made us feel as though we were taking part in a glorious parade for their special amusement. They swarmed after us, whooping with delight and asking innumerable questions about the weapons we carried. Apparently they had never seen guns and swords before.

"It was impossible to keep strict discipline, and I began to feel rather foolish. My soldiers answered the questions of the children, and I saw one old warrior throw a kiss to a little golden-haired tot on a doorstep. 'Just the size of my Lisa,' he muttered.

"Still no sign of ambush. We rode straight to the open square on which faced the town hall. Here, if anywhere, resistance was to be expected. This is what we found. The door of the beautiful old building was wide open. Pigeons flew up from the grass around the fountain as we approached. No cannon or barricade was in sight, and my regiment, as it poured into the square, looked out of place.

"Just as I had reached the hall and my guard was drawn up at attention, an old white-haired man, who by his insignia I surmised to be the mayor, stepped forth, followed by ten men in simple peasants' costume. They were all dignified and unabashed by the armed force before them— the most terrible soldiers of the great army of Austria."

"And what did this old man say, in the face of your guns and your cannon?" asked the little boy breathlessly.

"He walked down the steps, straight to my horse's side, and with hand extended, cried, 'Welcome, brother!' One of my aides made a gesture as if to strike him down with his sword, but I saw by the face of the old mayor that this was no trick on his part.

" 'Where are your soldiers?' I demanded.

" 'Soldiers? Why, don't you know we have none!' he replied in wonderment, as though I had said, 'Where are your giants?' or 'Where are your dwarfs?'

" 'But we have come to take the town.'

" 'Well, no one will stop you.'

" 'Are there none here to fight?'

"At this question, the old man's face lit up with a rare smile that I will always remember. Often afterwards, when engaged in bloody warfare, I would suddenly see that man's smile—and somehow, I came to hate my business. His words were simply:

" 'No, there is no one here to fight. We have chosen Christ for our Leader, and he taught men another way.' "

"What did you do then, grandfather?" asked the little boy eagerly.

"Do you know, son," the old soldier answered, "there seemed nothing left for us to do but to ride away, leaving the town unmolested. It was impossible to take it. If I had ordered my soldiers to fire on those smiling men, women and children, I knew they would not have obeyed me. Even military discipline has its limits. Could I command the grisly soldier to shoot down the child who reminded him of his Lisa? I reported to headquarters that the town had offered unassailable resistance, although this admission injured my military reputation. But I was right. We had literally been conquered by these simple folk who followed implicitly the leadership of Jesus Christ."

UNITED NATION

WHEN your grandmother's grandfather's grandmother was about your age, the thirteen states were in a peck of trouble.

It was because the United States weren't yet united; they weren't even called *United*. There was a loose string of an agreement, called the "Articles of Confederation," tied around them; but it could easily have slipped off, letting the States spill out in every direction. They might have turned into three or four different nations, or even eight or ten. They had several different kinds of governments, and they had already got into several quarrels with one another.

The war with England, their mother country, had lasted seven years. It was only four years now they had been at peace. And they felt anything but peaceful! Tired, edgy, hating to realize how run down their farms and houses were, and their stores and mills and schools, they probably also missed the excitement of war, much as they hated its danger and dirt and disease.

The first time they tried to hold a meeting, to which every State would send one or more representatives in an effort to combine into a real nation, it had been a complete failure. Nobody—literally nobody—came.

But there are generally one or two persons who continue trying. And so Benjamin Franklin and George Washington and several others kept on until they persuaded their discouraged neighbors to join in one more effort, and to meet in Philadelphia the first Monday in May, 1787.

Washington was there the first day. (You'd know he would be.) And though hardly anybody else came that day, he was there the next day. Again, hardly anybody came. You know how hard it is in such a situation not to say "Goodbye! I'm leaving!" Washington didn't leave. He came again the next day.

Washington kept a diary. In its pages he said right out how discouraged he felt. One day there would be perhaps two persons; the next day, maybe three; but the next, only one. Washington kept on coming, although one day he was the only one there. And on the twentieth day, enough were there, according to law, to do business.

So, having a quorum at last, they made Washington chairman. He said he didn't know much about being one, and hoped to be excused for any mistakes he made. The first thing the Convention did, was to lay down very careful rules to keep everybody polite and perfectly fair. How well these rules worked was another matter! But at least they honestly tried to guard against their own quarrelsomeness.

And then those delegates went to work, doubtful as most of them felt, to dig the cellar and lay the foundations for our country: its Constitution, its central laws—with which all later laws would have to agree—unless the whole country, by a sizeable majority, voted to change some part of the Constitution itself. They provided exactly how these changes *could* be made, when the people in general wanted them, without breaking or weakening the union of the country. And all the time they wondered, "CAN it possibly last?"

Three particularly hot disputes came up. The first was about slavery. That sore spot had started, you remember, only twelve years after the founding of our first settlement, Jamestown, when a Dutch captain dragged African natives to America and sold them to white owners. It had been going on now for one hundred and sixty-eight years, and still the ships kept coming.

The clerk read out, in his clear, slow, uninteresting voice,

"The importation of slaves shall not be prohibited by Congress before the year 1808. But a tax may be imposed, not exceeding ten dollars each slave."

"What's this I hear?" asked a Maryland member, (in more dignified words). Wilson, of Pennsylvania, got up.

"Frankly," he said (in substance) "it's what northern members, who *don't* want any more slaves brought in, and certain southern ones, who *do* want them, have agreed on. The northern men agree to let the slave trade go on twenty years more, and by that time the southern states will have all the slaves they need."

James Madison of Virginia said most Americans disliked the slave trade, and most of the states had already passed laws forbidding it. But, as a few states still wanted it, "well, if human beings are property, why, property can be taxed."

Baldwin of Georgia said, very quietly, that this branch of commerce was a delicate subject—better not discuss it— each state could pass what laws it wished—and when he sat down he carefully hadn't used the words "slave" or "slavery" a single time.

No matter how carefully words were chosen, the delegates were getting excited. They forgot their rules, scraped the floor with the legs of their chairs, interrupted each other. Washington had to use his gavel, and say,

"Gentlemen—gentlemen!"

Things quieted down, but soon boiled up again. It wasn't the north against the south—it was more mixed up than that. Robert Morris of Pennsylvania listened to the tumult awhile, and then said,

"The whole question is loaded with trouble for this country. Are these slaves property, or are they men?" If they were men, he added, why couldn't they vote?

Mason of Virginia said the New England sea-captains who made money by dragging men, women and children here to sell into slavery ought to be ashamed of themselves.

You see what a wasps' nest they were in the middle of; every section more or less mixed up in the sorry business, and yet honestly ashamed of it. Washington had to strike harder with his gavel, and say,

"Gentlemen! *GENTLEMEN!*"

Finally, after a great deal of argument, the law which the clerk had read out in the beginning did pass and was copied into the statute books.

This kind of give-and-take helped the delegates through the two still harder conflicts that came up later in the Convention.

After deciding, without any great difficulty, to have a president, they took up, unsuspectingly, the innocent-sounding question of how to elect him? Immediately they found themselves handling a roll of barbed wire.

Most of them believed in democracy—but it was frighteningly *new,* and untried. Of course the president ought to be chosen by a majority of his fellow-citizens. A splendid principle. But—"how very *ignorant* most poor workingmen are!" said the well-to-do, well-educated men who made up the Convention. (Nobody had as yet imagined such a thing as *women* voting.)

It is hard for us to remember that in those days there were no public schools, no state colleges; hardly any daily papers; no post-offices, or regular mails carried by the government; no telegraph or telephone; no trains or steamships; no broadcasting, wireless, television, or electric signs flashing in city streets. No public libraries!

Thus we can understand that they had reason to be afraid ignorance would cause serious mistakes.

And some of these educated men even seemed to think that these people, because they were poor, were probably dishonest!

King, of Massachusetts, said, "If we allow each penniless man to vote for president, the number of *votes for sale* will be like the sands of the sea. ."

Alexander Hamilton of New York thought so too; and Pinckney said, to put the choice of president "further away from the common man, we all agree is wise."

Well! Dangers terribly real and important to *them*, it's easy enough for us to laugh at now. *We* know their hard, discouraged plans succeeded! *They* saw those plans from the other end, and didn't know whether they would succeed or fail.

They made so little progress that, at the close of the session one day, when Washington asked,

"Does anyone wish to put a motion?" Morris said,

"Mr. President, the only motion that occurs to me, as suitable for this occasion, is that we give up and go home."

Washington then was inspired to say the greatest words —I think—he ever said:

"Gentlemen, it is too probable that *no* plan we propose will be adopted. But we *must stand firm* on the *best* in us. . . . Let us raise a standard to which the wise and honest can repair! *The event is in the hand of God.*"

And again they found a compromise way. Every man could vote—yes; but not for president. They could vote for an elector—some trusted fellow-citizen of their own state. And those thirteen electors would come together and choose a president, according to their wise opinions.

But now came on their worst problem of all—at least it roused the greatest partisanship. Beside every State's Legislature, there must also be a Legislature of the United States. They decided to call it Congress. How should its members be elected?

If every State sent just one representative, there might easily be more votes from the thinly populated states than from the populous ones. In that case, the minority would be ruling the majority. An upside-down way for having democracy! exclaimed the representatives of the big states.

Well, but if they were chosen according to population, the big states would *always* be the majority! and what would become of the little ones? They would only last as long as "an icicle in June!" said fiery Mr. Brearly of Delaware. "One representative from every state alike," demanded all the little states, declaring that otherwise they would soon be "gobbled up." "Rhode Island will be a county in Connecticut," they prophesied.

Amazed at these demonstrations of distrust and fear, the delegates from the large states protested that after all, a majority was a majority, and anybody who could count could prove it. Was Virginia to have no more representatives than Maryland? than Delaware? Why, she had sixteen times as many people as Delaware! Was a Virginian only one-sixteenth as good as a Delawarean?

This thunderstorm went on for two weeks or more.

When Paterson of the then sparsely settled New Jersey demanded, for the nth time, "One state, one vote," Wilson of Pennsylvania said:

"I see no reason to think States' Rights are the idol of this people. I wouldn't think it any comedown (or words to that effect) from being a citizen of Pennsylvania to being a citizen of the United States!" He received applause, but Lansing of New York (another sparsely settled state) said *his* state probably wouldn't have sent any representative if any such idea had been dreamed of! And the word "Liar" was heard.

Old Benjamin Franklin rose.

Washington said, "Gentlemen, Dr. Franklin wishes to address you."

Franklin spoke first about the shared dangers of the war, the danger the infant Republic was still in, touching skilfully on their common love of country; and as he talked, the delegates began to feel like one family. Then he said what a *small* thing, compared with the cause of freedom, and the past efforts they had made for it, was now dividing them!

"What is it? a mere detail! Shall we confess ourselves beaten by a difference of opinion over a detail?" It was eloquent, moving; but what he next said was a hundred times more so.

"May I make a statement of my own position? I've felt from the beginning that we should be represented according to population. I've voted with the larger states, convinced that I was right. But, gentlemen, as this debate has run on, a great IDEA has come to me—the idea that I MIGHT BE WRONG!

"Gentlemen," he went on, "we have been trying, like wilful children, each to get his own way . . . it came over me today like a conviction of sin. Look into your hearts, my brothers, and see if you don't find the same fault there."

It must have been like a spring thaw in a frozen river, his saying that. He went on to suggest:

"—that we now adjourn for the rest of the day . . . (and) each one of us spend every waking hour . . . until we reconvene tomorrow, *not* with those who agree with us, planning how to win, but in humble, open, sincere talk with men of the opposite opinion, trying to invent some way in which *both sides may win*. Mr. President, I move we adjourn."

Dozens seconded the motion. Washington, lightly touching his gavel to the table, said "The motion is carried." He and Franklin went out together.

Whether Wilson and Mason talked with Brearly and Lansing that night, and with whom Franklin and Washington talked, we can only guess; but it wasn't long before the luminously simple inspiration developed, of having two Houses of Congress; every state having the same numer of Senators, regardless of population; and representatives to the House elected one to every so many thousand.

And that was the way that both sides won!

Sarah N. Cleghorn

A QUAKER WEDDING

On a sunshiny day in May 1763, a hum of preparation was going on in the stone farmhouse which was the home of Joseph Burr, near Mt. Holly, New Jersey. The excitement was somewhat subdued, for Joseph Burr and his family were Quakers, and took their pleasures quietly. But the rich fruitcake and baked ham and syrupy sweet potatoes were plentiful wedding fare, and furniture and copper and pewter shone with the vigorous polishing which the young bride had given them.

Two things were unusual about this wedding. One was that it was not held in the Meeting House on Woodpecker Lane but at Peachfields, the pleasant home of Joseph Burr. The other was that the bride, Dido, and the groom, William Boen, were Negroes, and so also were fifteen of the wedding guests. In those days in that neighborhood dark skins usually belonged to slaves, who were more likely to be serving their master's guests, than to be themselves guests in a well-to-do household.

Today the bride herself was an ex-slave, Dido, who had belonged to Joseph Burr since she was thirteen. To Quakers, however, who firmly believe that there is "that of God in every man," the thought of one person's actually owning another person, was an uncomfortable one. No doubt Joseph Burr had often had his attention called to this matter by his nephew John Woolman, a gentle but firm young man who felt a particular tenderness for any creatures who suffered, and who believed that the fact of owning slaves, no matter how well they were treated, damaged both the master and the slave. And so Joseph Burr had recently given Dido her liberty. Peachfields had become home to her. She was treated well, so since her freedom she had worked on there and saved her money for the day when she and William might be married.

Her friendship with William Boen had been a long-standing affair. As children they had played together on the large farm of their master, Moses Haines. Play-time was short for slave—children, and schools for Negroes did not exist. Spelling and geography were not for Dido, but she learned excellently to sweep and clean and keep the house neat, and when she knew how to bake bread in the brick oven alongside the wide old fireplace, and cook a savory stew in the great heavy iron kettle, she was very valuable, worth at least $200.00.

When she was thirteen years old Dido was sold, away from her mother, her old home, and her best friend William Boen, to Joseph Burr of Peachfields. William cheered her by saying, "Never mind, Dido, we'll see each other often. Peachfields is not far, and before long I'll be allowed to drive Ned and Dolly and bring our folks to see Joseph Burr and his family. Then we can see each other too, Dido. Don't cry."

And so, indeed, it happened. The Haines family often went to visit the Burrs at Peachfields, with William driving the two handsome bay horses, Ned and Dolly, and William and Dido could visit in the big kitchen in winter or stand talking by the pasture fence in summer. Often Joseph Burr's nephew, John Woolman, rode over to call on Moses Haines and his family. Sometimes, with the approval of his host, he would excuse himself after dinner and go to find his young friend William Boen and give him a lesson in reading and writing. William was an eager pupil and learned quickly and well. He learned, too, to enjoy going to Friends' Meeting. Whenever he drove his master and mistress to the meeting for worship in Mt. Holly, William was allowed to come in and sit on the back bench. He loved the silence, and in heart and mind he became a Quaker, but so deeply rooted were master-slave customs and thought even among the Friends, that the meeting did not until years later feel it right to accept him as a member.

John Woolman worked hard on behalf of William's freedom, and in this undertaking he was successful. Moses Haines signed his name to a paper which Woolman drew up, stating that at the age of thirty William Boen would be a free man. Furthermore, it stated, William was welcome to stay on at his old job at good pay. In the meantime, as we have seen, Dido had already been given her freedom, and the happy friendship between her and her William had gone on. When William was twenty-eight there seemed no reason to postpone their marriage any longer, although William would be a slave for two years more. William, who had learned to love the Friends' way of worship, wanted a Quaker wedding, but to the more conservative members of the Meeting it seemed a revolutionary idea to use the Meeting House for the marriage of a slave and an ex-slave.

Once again John Woolman helped. He persuaded his uncle Joseph Burr that since Dido had lived in his family for so many years, it would be a friendly fatherly deed for him to invite the guests to Peachfields.

And so it came about that these two young people, devoted to each other and to their families, both white and black, were seated, on this spring morning in the big room at Peachfields. After sitting quietly together for a while, with the deep silence flowing about them like a river, Dido and William Boen stood up and taking each other by the hand, plighted their love. First William spoke, "In the presence of the Lord, and before these our friends, I take thee, Dido, to be my wife, promising with divine assistance to be unto thee a loving and faithful husband until death shall separate us."

Then Dido looked into the eyes of the man she had loved and trusted since their brief childhood, and said, "In the presence of the Lord, and before these our friends, I take thee, William Boen, to be my husband, promising with divine assistance, to be unto thee a loving and faithful wife until death shall separate us."

Again they sat down. Perhaps, out of the silence that followed, John Woolman or Patience Haines spoke a word of blessing on the young couple or voiced a prayer to our Heavenly Father. The certificate that John Woolman wrote out in his clear, careful, beautiful handwriting can still be seen today. On it are the signatures of those who witnessed the wedding, the names of twelve white Quakers, and fifteen Negro signatures, or marks for them, for some had never learned to write.

Out of doors on that day so long ago, apple blossoms in the orchards and sweet violets in the nearby woods, framed the wedding day in beauty. The family and friends gathered inside the house, in spite of difference of color and condition, were drawn close together in genuine well-wishing for the young couple, and in the worship of God. And, William and Dido lived happily together to the end of their days.

Adapted from Janet Whitney's John Woolman: American Quaker *by permission of Little Brown.*

HOW MUCH LAND
DOES A MAN NEED?

THIS is the story of Pahóm, a Russian peasant, whose only trouble was that he had not land enough.

Close to Pahóm's homestead there lived a lady, a small landowner, who had an estate of about three hundred acres. She had always lived on good terms with the peasants, until she engaged as her steward an old soldier, who took to burdening the people with fines. However careful Pahóm tried to be, it happened again and again that now a horse of his got among the lady's oats, now a cow strayed into her garden, now his calves found their way into her meadows—and he always had to pay a fine.

Pahóm paid up, but grumbled, and, going home in a temper, was rough with his family. All through that summer, Pahóm had much trouble because of this steward; and he was even glad when winter came and the cattle had to be stabled.

In the winter the news got about that the lady was going to sell her land, and that the keeper of the inn on the high road was bargaining for it. When the peasants heard this they were very much alarmed.

They tried to arrange for the Commune to buy the whole estate, so that it might be held by them all in common. They met twice to discuss it, but could not come to any agreement. So they decided to buy the land individually, each according to his means; and the lady agreed to this plan.

Pahóm and his wife put their heads together and considered how they could manage to buy some of the land.

They had one hundred roubles laid by. They sold a colt, and one half of their bees; hired out one of their sons as a labourer, and took his wages in advance; borrowed the rest from a brother-in-law, and so scraped together half the purchase money.

Having done this, Pahóm chose out a farm of forty acres, some of it wooded, and went to the lady to bargain for it. They came to an agreement and he paid her half the price down and promised to pay the remainder within two years.

So now Pahóm had land of his own. When he went out to plough his fields, or to look at his growing corn, or at his grassmeadows, his heart would fill with joy. The grass that grew and the flowers that bloomed there, seemed to him unlike any that grew elsewhere.

So Pahóm was well-contented, and everything would have been right if the neighboring peasants would only not have trespassed on his corn-fields and meadows. He appealed to them most civilly, but they still went on: now the Communal herdsmen would let the village cows stray into his meadows; then horses from the night pasture would get among his corn. Pahóm turned them out again and again, and forgave their owners, and for a long time he forbore from prosecuting any one. But at last he lost patience and complained to the District Court. He knew it was the peasants' want of land, and no evil intent on their part, that caused the trouble; but he thought:

"I cannot go on overlooking it, or they will destroy all I have. They must be taught a lesson."

So he had them up, gave them one lesson, and then another, and two or three of the peasants were fined. After a time Pahóm's neighbours began to bear him a grudge for this, and would now and then let their cattle onto his land on purpose.

About this time a rumour got about that many people were moving to new parts.

"There's no need for me to leave my land," thought Pahóm. "But some of the others might leave our village, and then there would be more room for us."

One day Pahóm was sitting at home, when a peasant, passing through the village, happened to call in. He was allowed to stay the night, and supper was given him. Pahóm had a talk with this peasant and asked him where he came from. The stranger answered that he came from beyond the Volga, where he had been working. One word led to another, and the man went on to say that many people were settling in those parts. He told how some people from his village had settled there. They had joined the Commune, and had had twenty-five acres per man granted them. The land was so good, he said, that the rye sown on it grew as high as a horse, and so thick that five sweeps of a sickle made a sheaf.

Pahóm's heart kindled with desire. He thought: "Why should I suffer in this narrow hole, if one can live so well elsewhere? I will sell my land and my homestead here, and with the money I will start afresh over there and get everything new. In this crowded place one is always having trouble. But I must first go and find out all about it myself."

Towards summer he got ready and started. He went down the Volga on a steamer to Samára, then walked another three hundred miles, and at last reached the place. It was just as the stranger had said.

Having found out all he wished to know, Pahóm returned home as autumn came on, and began selling off his belongings. He sold his land at a profit, sold his homestead and all his cattle, and withdrew from membership of the Commune. He only waited till the spring, and then started with his family for the new settlement.

As soon as Pahóm and his family arrived at their new abode, he applied for admission into the Commune of a large village. Five shares of Communal land were given him for his own and his sons' use: that is to say—125 acres (not all together, but in different fields) besides the use of the Communal pasture. Pahóm put up the buildings he needed, and bought cattle. He was ten times better off than he had been. He had plenty of arable land and pasturage, and could keep as many head of cattle as he liked.

At first, in the bustle of building and settling down, Pahóm was pleased with it all, but when he got used to it, he began to think that even here he had not enough land. Pahóm wanted to sow more wheat; so he rented land from a dealer for a year. He sowed much wheat and had a fine crop, but the land was too far from the village —the wheat had to be carted more than ten miles. After a time Pahóm noticed that some peasant-dealers were living on separate farms, and were growing wealthy; and he thought:

"If I were to buy some freehold land and have a homestead on it, it would be a different thing altogether. Then it would all be nice and compact."

So Pahóm began looking out for land which he could buy; and he came across a peasant who had bought thirteen hundred acres, but having got into difficulties was willing to sell again cheap. Pahóm bargained and haggled with him, and at last they settled the price at 1,500 roubles, part in cash and part to be paid later. They had all but clinched the matter, when a passing dealer happened to stop at Pahóm's one day to get a feed for his horses. He drank tea with Pahóm, and they had a talk. The dealer said that he was just returning from the land of the Bashkirs, far away, where he had bought thirteen thousand

acres of land, all for 1,000 roubles. Pahóm questioned him
further, and the tradesman said:

"All one need do is to make friends with the chiefs. I
gave away about one hundred roubles' worth of dressing-
gowns and carpets, besides a case of tea, and I got the land
for almost nothing."

Pahóm inquired how to get to the place, and as soon
as the tradesman had left him, he prepared to go there
himself. He left his wife to look after the homestead, and
started on his journey taking his man with him. They
stopped at a town on their way, and bought a case of tea,
and other presents, as the tradesman had advised. On and
on they went until they had gone more than three hundred miles, and on the seventh day they came to a place
where the Bashkirs had pitched their tents. It was all just
as the tradesman had said. The people lived on the steppes,
by a river, in felt-covered tents. They neither tilled the
ground, nor ate bread. Their cattle and horses grazed in
herds on the steppe. They were quite ignorant, and knew
no Russian, but were good-natured enough.

As soon as they saw Pahóm, they came out of their tents
and gathered round their visitor. An interpreter was found,
and Pahóm told them he had come about some land. The
Bashkirs seemed very glad; they took Pahóm and led him
into one of the best tents, where they made him sit on
some down cushions placed on a carpet, while they sat
round him. They gave him tea and kumiss, and had a
sheep killed, and gave him mutton to eat. Pahóm took
presents out of his cart and distributed them among the
Bashkirs, and divided amongst them the tea. The Bashkirs were delighted. They talked a great deal among themselves, and then told the interpreter to translate.

"They wish me to tell you," said the interpreter, "that
in return for your presents they will gladly give you as

much land as you want. You have only to point it out with your hand and it is yours."

The Bashkirs talked again for a while and began to dispute. Pahóm asked what they were disputing about, and the interpreter told him that some of them thought they ought to ask their Chief about the land and not act in his absence.

While the Bashkirs were disputing, a man in a large fox-fur cap appeared on the scene. They all became silent and rose to their feet. The interpreter said, "This is our Chief himself."

Pahóm immediately fetched the best dressing-gown and five pounds of tea, and offered these to the Chief. The Chief accepted them, and seated himself in the place of honour. The Bashkirs at once began telling him something. The Chief listened for a while, then made a sign with his head for them to be silent, and addressing himself to Pahóm, said in Russian:

"Well, let it be so. Choose whatever piece of land you like; we have plenty of it."

"And what will be the price?" asked Pahóm.

"Our price is always the same: one thousand roubles a day."

Pahóm did not understand.

"A day? What measure is that? How many acres would that be?"

"We do not know how to reckon it out," said the Chief. "We sell it by the day. As much as you can go round on your feet in a day is yours, and the price is one thousand roubles a day."

Pahóm was surprised.

"But in a day you can get round a large tract of land," he said.

The Chief laughed.

"It will all be yours!" said he. "But there is one condition: if you don't return on the same day to the spot whence you started, your money is lost."

"But how am I to mark the way that I have gone?"

"Why, we shall go to any spot you like, and stay there. You must start from that spot and make your round, taking a spade with you. Wherever you think necesary, make a mark. At every turning, dig a hole and pile up the turf; then afterwards we will go round with a plough from hole to hole. You may make as large a circuit as you please, but before the sun sets you must return to the place you started from. All the land you cover will be yours."

Pahóm was delighted. It was decided to start early next morning. They gave Pahóm a feather-bed to sleep on, and the Bashkirs dispersed for the night, promising to assemble the next morning at daybreak and ride out before sunrise to the appointed spot.

Pahóm lay on the feather-bed, but could not sleep. He kept thinking about the land.

"What a large tract I will mark off!" thought he. "I can easily do thirty-five miles in a day. The days are long now, and within a circuit of thirty-five miles what a lot of land there will be! I will sell the poorer land, or let it to peasants, but I'll pick out the best and farm it. I will buy two ox-teams, and hire two more labourers. About a hundred and fifty acres shall be plough-land, and I will pasture cattle on the rest."

At last he saw that the dawn was breaking.

He got up, roused his man and went to call the Bashkirs.

"It's time to go to the steppe to measure the land," he said.

The Bashkirs got ready and they all started: some mounted on horses, and some in carts. Pahóm drove in his own small cart with his servant, and took a spade with him. When they reached the steppe, the morning red was beginning to kindle. They ascended a hillock and dismounting from their carts and their horses, gathered in one spot. The Chief came up to Pahóm and stretching out his arm towards the plain:

"See," said he, "all this, as far as your eye can reach, is ours. You may have any part of it you like."

Pahóm's eyes glistened: It was all virgin soil, as flat as the palm of your hand, as black as the seed of a poppy, and in the hollows different kinds of grasses grew breast high.

The Chief took off his fox-fur cap, placed it on the ground and said:

"This will be the mark. Start from here, and return here again. All the land you go round shall be yours."

Pahóm took out his money and put it on the cap. Then he took off his outer coat, remaining in his sleeveless undercoat. He unfastened his girdle and tied it tight below his stomach, put a little bag of bread into the breast of his coat, and tying a flask of water to his girdle, he drew up the tops of his boots, took the spade from his man, and stood ready to start. He considered for some moments which way he had better go—it was tempting everywhere.

"No matter," he concluded, "I will go towards the rising sun."

He turned his face to the east, stretched himself and waited for the sun to appear above the rim.

The sun's rays had hardly flashed above the horizon before Pahóm, carrying the spade over his shoulder, went down into the steppe.

Pahóm started walking neither slowly nor quickly. After having gone a thousand yards he stopped, dug a hole, and placed pieces of turf one on another to make it more visible. Then he went on; and now that he had walked off his stiffness he quickened his pace. After a while he dug another hole.

Pahóm looked back. The hillock could be distinctly seen in the sunlight, with the people on it, and the glittering tyres of the cart-wheels. At a rough guess Pahóm concluded that he had walked three miles. It was growing warmer; he took off his under-coat, flung it across his shoulder, and went on again. It had grown quite warm now; he looked at the sun, it was time to think of breakfast.

He sat down, took off his boots, stuck them into his girdle, and went on. It was easy walking now.

"I will go on for another three miles," thought he, "and then turn to the left. This spot is so fine, that it would be a pity to lose it. The further one goes, the better the land seems."

He went straight on for a while, and when he looked round, the hillock was scarcely visible and the people on it looked like black ants, and he could just see something glistening there in the sun.

"Ah," thought Pahóm, "I have gone far enough in this direction, it is time to turn."

He stopped, dug a large hole, and heaped up pieces of turf. Next he untied his flask, had a drink, and then turned sharply to the left. He went on and on; the grass was high, and it was very hot.

Pahóm began to grow tired: he looked at the sun and saw that it was noon.

"Well," he thought, "I must have a rest."

He sat down, and ate some bread and drank some water; but he did not lie down, thinking that if he did he might fall asleep. After sitting a little while, he went on again. At first he walked easily: the food had strengthened him; but it had become terribly hot, and he felt sleepy; still he went on, thinking: "An hour to suffer, a lifetime to live."

He went a long way in this direction also, and was about to turn to the left again, when he perceived a damp hollow: "It would be a pity to leave that out," he thought. "Flax would do well there." So he went on past the hollow, and dug a hole on the other side of it before he turned the corner. Pahóm looked towards the hillock. The heat made the air hazy: it seemed to be quivering, and through the haze the people on the hillock could scarcely be seen.

"Ah!" thought Pahóm, "I have made the sides too long; I must make this one shorter." And he went along the third side, stepping faster. He looked at the sun: it was nearly half way to the horizon, and he had not yet done two miles of the third side of the square. He was still ten miles from the goal.

"No," he thought, "though it will make my land lopsided, I must hurry back in a straight line now. I might go too far, and as it is I have a great deal of land."

So Pahóm hurriedly dug a hole, and turned straight towards the hillock.

Pahóm now walked with difficulty. He was done up with the heat, his bare feet were cut and bruised, and his legs began to fail. He longed to rest, but it was impossible if he meant to get back before sunset. The sun waits for no man, and it was sinking lower and lower.

"Oh dear," he thought, "if only I have not blundered trying for too much! What if I am too late?"

He began running, threw away his coat, his boots, his flask, and his cap, and kept only the spade which he used as a support.

His breast was working like a blacksmith's bellows, his heart was beating like a hammer, and his legs were giving way as if they did not belong to him. Pahóm was seized with terror lest he should die of the strain.

The sun was quite low now, but he was also quite near

his aim. Pahóm could already see the people on the hillock waving their arms to hurry him up. He could see the fox-fur cap on the ground, and the money on it, and the Chief sitting on the ground.

"There is plenty of land," thought he, "but will God let me live on it? I have lost my life, I have lost my life! I shall never reach that spot!"

Pahóm looked at the sun, which had reached the earth: one side of it had already disappeared. With all his remaining strength he rushed on, bending his body forward so that his legs could hardly follow fast enough to keep him from falling. Just as he reached the hillock it suddenly grew dark. He looked up—the sun had already set! He gave a cry: and was about to stop, but he heard the Bashkirs still shouting, and remembered that though to him, from below, the sun seemed to have set, they on the hillock could still see it. He took a long breath and ran up the hillock. It was still light there. He reached the top and saw the cap. Before it sat the Chief laughing and holding his sides. Pahóm legs gave way beneath him, he fell forward and reached the cap with his hands.

"Ah, that's a fine fellow!" exclaimed the Chief. "He has gained much land!"

Pahóm's servant came running up and tried to raise him, but he saw that blood was flowing from his mouth. Pahóm was dead!

The Bashkirs clicked their tongues to show their pity.

His servant picked up the spade and dug a grave long enough for Pahóm to lie in, and buried him in it. Six feet from his head to his heels was all he needed.

Abbreviated and adapted from the Maude translation of Tolstóy's Twenty-three Tales, in the Oxford University Press, "World Classics" series.

THE stillness was so complete that a large buzzing fly making clumsy progress up one of the high, north windows seemed to have appropriated the big, bare white room as a sounding-board. Karen followed its movements fascinated. It would blunder a zig-zag course up one of the long panes and then, just as it was climbing the wooden moulding to scale still dizzier heights, it would lose its foothold and fall bumbling noisily down to the bottom of the window. Half a dozen times the whole difficult ascent was repeated. The fifth time up, Karen, who had been reading Hawthorne's tales from Greek legends, named the noisy object of her interest, Sisyphus, because of the patience and persistence of its vain endeavors. And she offered imaginary prizes. If Sisyphus should manage to clear the two longest panes, she would give a party in his honor of sugar and water to a group of flies on the nursery window-sill; and if Sisyphus should actually reach the more difficult wedge-shaped panes in the arch right at the top of the window, then—then Karen would make a vow to catch no more flies to feed to her pet lizards, who must be content henceforth with other food. This would be Karen's tribute of respect to the steadfastness of Sisyphus.

The sixth attempt *was* actually successful. Karen held her breath as Sisyphus toiled unsteadily up through the fan-shaped window-arch to the very top—where Doom awaited him—a spider-web! Suddenly the drowsy buzzing gave place to shrill, agonized sounds, like screams for help. They rose in a steady crescendo and seemed to fill the big, white spaces of the Meeting-House. So loud they were, it seemed momentarily that either Sarah Coffin or Hester

Starr, who sat near the window on the "facing benches," *must* give some sign of awareness of such unusual commotion. Unlike Deborah Shoemaker, who sat at the very head of the Meeting, right under the window—*they* were not hard of hearing.

But no; all those quiet faces of ministers and elders, under the stiff Quaker bonnets, were wrapt in deep meditation, as still as the hands folded across the fresh, white tuckers and the gray and fawn-colored shawls.

It was a mystery to Karen, as her eyes traveled along the rows of unseeing faces, how human beings could be so completely unconscious of everything around them. Friends' Meeting was rather like the palace of the Sleeping Beauty after the angry fairy had waved her wand—only *these* were such odd-looking people to be held bewitched by such a magic spell. There was nothing to suggest a fairy's wand about Thomas Jones's long, melancholy nose and his hair parted in the middle and falling down behind the ears like an old portrait of George Fox or John Woolman; nor about Joseph Taylor's short bang across his forehead, his old-fashioned neckcloth and broad-brimmed beaver hat.

But there they were, all lost in a deep common reverie. It was not like sleep, though Karen had her moments of alarm lest Joseph Taylor's eyes *might* be closed in sleep, a danger Karen didn't dare to think of—for on Joseph Taylor depended the whole responsibility of *closing the Meeting*. What if some day it *should* be sleep and they should all be doomed to sit on for endless hours until Joseph Taylor should awake! Generally, there was some queer inner sense of the passing of time that, at about twelve o'clock, made Joseph Taylor open his eyes, turn to the Friend seated nearest him on the "facing benches" and shake hands. It was the charm that broke the spell; all the unseeing faces became friendly and welcoming and the whole place was, all at once, astir.

But before this return to reality, there were endless stretches of restlessness and boredom to which Karen looked forward with dread most of the week. "Going to Meeting with Grandmamma" was part of the general order of things—as unavoidable as arithmetic lessons or the dentist—that just had to be gone through with, no matter how unwillingly.

In the first place, there were the unmerciful wooden benches. They were so broad that if Karen sat all the way in on the grey cushions against the hard, high back, her feet stuck straight out in front of her at an angle that presently produced prickles up and down her legs until one leg or the other went quite asleep and had to be pinched back to life again. Then, if she slid ever so gently forward (Grandmamma disapproved of wriggling) so that the numb feet and legs could hang downwards, the relief of that did not last long, for soon the uneasy sensations moved up to her bony little shoulder-blades that, without support, kept hunching themselves over more and more, despite the grown-ups' frequent reminders to "sit up straight." But far worse than the aching shoulders were the sudden "growing pains" that would seize one of the legs hanging in mid-air and that demanded instant relief. And despite Grandmamma's warning hand reached out and laid upon hers, she *had* to wriggle about sideways and curl the offending member up under her to ease the pain. Nowhere else but in Meeting did Karen ever suffer so many physical discomforts—sudden toothaches, coughs to smother or sneezes that threatened to break the silence with what, to her shyness, seemed loud, disturbing sounds. At all other times she was too busy and interested to really be aware of her body at all.

Here at Meeting, trying to forget these physical difficulties, Karen would send her thoughts in search of distraction, across the rows of bowed heads against the white benches, out to the glimpse of trees and sky beyond the high, bare windows. In mild weather, when the windows stood open, there would come sounds of twittering and singing in the leafy branches and lively voices shouting from a playground near by; church bells near and far, and sometimes organ music and the verses of hymns floating out from the Presbyterian church a block away. Some of the verses she knew and she could join silently in the singing. This brought her memories of services she had sometimes been invited to attend with great-aunt Anna Fenwick (who was not a Friend), services in the Episcopal church. These had seemed to her models of order, of interest and of beauty. The constant activity—standing, sitting, kneeling, singing, finding places in prayer-book and hymnal—were a welcome outlet for her childish restlessness. Even the sermons, though rather tedious and containing many mysterious allusions to which her Quaker upbringing gave her no clue: (the Holy Trinity, the Blood of the Atonement, the Holy Ghost, the Resurrection of the Body)—even these fitted into the order of the whole service and were delivered in an appropriate style.

But in Meeting, sermons were endless and roused in Karen anything from tedium to alarm. There were exceptions. When Rachel Wallace rose to speak, Karen always felt reassured. She spoke in a clear, fresh voice—a few simple precepts drawn from a passage of scripture; and she looked so pretty and silvery in her grey dress and crisp white cap and tucker, she was a pleasure to see and hear. Also, her little sermons were short. But when the Spirit moved Isaac Stratton (as it generally did), Karen was filled with anxiety. You never could tell *when* Isaac Stratton's sermons would come to an end.

Today, just as Karen's anxiety over the struggles of Sisyphus was at its height, Isaac Stratton took a large, red cotton handkerchief out of the crown of his broad-brimmed hat, mopped his brow in preparation, and rose to speak. Karen gave a drowning glance in the direction of Joseph Taylor (who might, with luck, *almost* have been ready to "close the meeting"), and settled down to a long ordeal.

Isaac Stratton began, as usual, in even, ordinary tones: "Hath not God made foolish the wisdom of this world? For after that in the wisdom of God the world by wisdom knew not God, it pleased God by the foolishness of preaching to save them that believe." Karen pricked up her ears. Scriptural language was generally rather confusing to her; but that Isaac Stratton should be admitting "the foolishness of preaching" was hopeful; was it possible he was going to turn over a new leaf?

However, her hope faded as the voice rose out of its everyday pitch in a continuing crescendo to a sort of singsong chant, then to a strange nasal whine and on up to a shrill falsetto that made Karen think of the Bible tales of people possessed by a demon. Surely some uncanny spirit had taken possession of Isaac Stratton! Then, all at once, the demon was silent, there was a pause, and the voice would go back to a natural tone, only to climb again in the same chanting sing-song. Karen lost all notion of what Isaac Stratton was saying, but she was carried along by the rhythm and the weird tones, almost as if she had a share in them; her face burning with embarrassment. Long before Isaac Stratton's inspiration had spent itself, Karen was quivering with anxiety over how and when it would end, her hands icy, her cheeks aflame. Isaac Stratton's sermons were her worst ordeal at Meeting. But today—as on other occasions—long after she had given up hope, there he was, seated again, his face as quiet and serene as if the mystery that had just possessed him had been merely her imagination.

Certainly, there was something very different about all this from the planned and orderly ceremonial that had given her in the Episcopal service such a sense of reassurance. She dimly sensed something deep and mysterious about the Quaker Meeting. What went on behind those rows of rapt faces filled her with awe, but also with alarm. It was beyond the understanding of a child, these mystic, personal experiences. And with her need for security, for external loveliness, her thoughts turned wistfully on Sundays to the bright altar with its tapers and flowers, the stained glass windows, the vestments and the ceremonial beauty of the church service that had won her heart.

Well—here she sat now, wrapped once more in the deep, mysterious silence—her eyes fixed desperately on Joseph Taylor's still unconscious face. *Was* he asleep? Would he wake in time? A great sigh escaped her as he slowly opened his eyes. He turned and gave his hand to Samuel Shute. It was like an electric current. The strangeness and the mystery were at an end. These were all ordinary human beings once more, smiling and much interested in each others' health and welfare.

Now, Karen had a fresh anxiety—to remain, if possible, unnoticed behind Grandmamma's ample draperies, and so slip away without shaking hands with Joseph Taylor. Joseph Taylor was a bluff farmer with a weather-beaten face and tremendous, powerful hands. His friendliness included not only grown-ups, but children, for whom he seemed to have a special liking and, on catching sight of Karen, he would forge forward with outstretched hands and clasp her small bony fingers in a terrible, crushing grip that, with tightly pressed lips, she just managed to endure without an outcry of pain. All the way home after such a painful greeting, Karen's hand would throb and ache. Decidedly, it was best after Meeting not to catch Joseph Taylor's eye. Karen lingered a few minutes on the safe side of Grandmamma; but Grandmamma was busy discussing with two other Friends some arrangements for Quarterly Meeting. That would take time. It would be safer if Karen should slip in among the groups moving toward the door and wait for Grandmamma safely with John in the carriage outside.

As Karen came through the Meeting House gate toward the waiting carriage, there approached with somewhat mincing steps a figure of—to Karen—rather embarrassing elegance, Florrie Miller, one of the more dazzling members of Karen's dancing-class. Florrie, though not much older than Karen, was, in dress, manners and general sophistication, almost of another generation. She was always adorned with clusters of curls, with lockets, bracelets and bangles (Karen had heard them rattling scornfully when, at the last dancing-lesson Karen and Elspeth had been invited by Signor Passetto to demonstrate a difficult step for the entire class); and Florrie's superiority in the matter of fashionable attire was unquestionable. Indeed, superiority was Florrie's special gift. One slow, measuring look from her could reduce Karen to the most abject sense that everything about her was all wrong—her simple speech, her simple manners and, above all, her simple clothes. To grown-ups her smocked "Liberty" frocks, woolen jerseys and Eton collars might seem neat and picturesque, but under Florrie's measuring eye, Karen knew that they were simply outlandish. And this Sunday morning, as Florrie bore down on her, resplendent in a feathered hat and modish costume Karen was again overcome by the sense of her own inferiority.

However, the last time they had met, Florrie had been

quite condescendingly friendly. It had been a rainy afternoon and Karen and Elspeth had offered her a lift in the
carriage. So now, as she passed, Karen turned her a timid
smile of greeting. The smile froze to a sort of vacancy as
she realized that Florrie had looked her straight in the face
and *stuck out her tongue* as, with a toss of her curls and a
swish of her skirt, she passed on her way.

Forlornness overcame Karen as she crouched in a corner
of the carriage behind John's broad back. What was the
use of hoping and trying to be friends with someone who
was too different from you? Even if *you* wanted to try to
forget it, they wouldn't let you. They'd always remind you,
as Florrie had just done, that you were an outsider, that
you didn't belong.

It was the central fact of Karen's existence; she was always some sort of an outsider. She felt she didn't really
belong anywhere. The roots of it lay far back—above all in
Karen's Quaker ancestry. Non-conformity in speech and
dress and conduct was in her blood. Her forbears, intent
on applying Christianity to life, had defied the conventions
and challenged the abuses and cruelties of society and suffered persecution for it, and even death. Anti-slavery,
prison reform, woman suffrage, anti-militarism; their cham-
pionship of unpopular causes had kept them always at odds
with the established order of things; and society, like Florrie, had stuck its tongue out at them for their unconven-
tionality, even when it respected their courage and
idealism.

In such a state of mind and feeling, there was a danger
that Karen might shrink away from natural social relations
with other people and become a self-centered little recluse;
but an experience just at this time in her shy and rather
lonely childhood, shook her suddenly out of her self-pity
and stirred in her another sort of pity—a pity and compas-

sion so generous and self-forgetful that it became a turning-point in her life.

It was all because of Joey.

Joey was the gay, smiling, dark-skinned and woolly-haired son of Albert—Albert who long before, during the Civil War had sought refuge from slavery in Grandpapa's home, a station on the "Underground Railway." Grandpapa had made possible his escape across the border into Canada. After the war he had come back, full of love and gratitude, begging to be allowed to stay near his benefactor and serve him always. Grandpapa had helped to start him in a little independent business of his own; and Albert, deft and handy, was now much in demand in the neighborhood to upholster chairs, clean carpets and repair furniture.

When Albert came to make slip covers or lay a stair-carpet for Grandmamma, he brought his small son, Joey, to keep him supplied with tools and nails and otherwise to fetch and carry, and they came often to Fenwick Farm during Spring and Autumn cleaning and renovation. Joey was always welcome. He was as spry and deft and willing as his father, and Grandmamma found him a very useful errand-boy. At the seasons when fruit was ripe, she would pay him to climb her cherry and mulberry trees and gather fruit for canning. He helped Karen to climb with him and she loved these fruit-picking bees and Joey's lively chatter and his gay, infectious laughter. He taught her to whistle clear and true, like a boy—an accomplishment she was proud of (though Grandmamma *did* think it unladylike).

Perched among the limbs of the big cherry-tree, they would whistle together "Old Black Joe," "Swanee River," "Ole Virginny" and the other tunes in Joey's endless repertory. Also he taught her to play "Dixie" and "Oh, Susannah" on the little mouth-organ he always carried in his pocket. And, in the intervals of Joey's more important duties, they played marbles and hop-scotch, turned hand-springs and did double-shuffles up and down the garden walk. The days Joey came to Fenwick Farm were days of complete enjoyment for Karen.

So when, the week before Karen's tenth birthday, Mamma raised the question of what children she would like to invite to her birthday party, she cried eagerly, "Oh, Joey, of course!" Mamma shook her head and, in the tone Mamma could use on occasion, a tone so firm it encouraged no argument, she replied, "No, Karen—that wouldn't be possible." And she went on to suggest instead, Stephen and Charlie and Fred—some of Karen's partners at dancing-school. Karen didn't like Stephen; he made faces at her when no one was looking; and the others teased her or tweaked her pig-tails from behind or mimicked her uncon-scious English accent. But she didn't like complaining of other children to grown-ups (it was part of Miss Griggs' code of "sportsmanlike behavior"): so, meekly, she pleaded, "Let's just invite *girls,* Mamma, then we can play with our dolls." There was no point in explaining that what she *really* enjoyed was the boys' games Joey had taught her and that she didn't care at all about playing with dolls. She had been trained not to argue with her elders; so the matter ended there, and only little girls came to Karen's birthday party.

But deep inside somewhere the question twisted and turned: *"Why?* Why was it impossible to invite Joey, her favorite playmate, to her birthday party?"

Then one day, after they had picked a big bowlful of raspberries in the garden and brought them in to Maggie, Karen and Joey were playing hop-scotch along the brick walk by the kitchen porch. Karen's back was turned so she didn't see Stephen come around the corner under the library windows. And of course she couldn't know that Stephen was cross because his mother, when she had sent him on an errand to Grandmamma, had forbidden his stopping for an hour's play at Fenwick Farm, and had told him instead to come straight back with Grandmamma's reply. Stephen, rebellious, had just been starting glumly for home with Grandmamma's letter crammed in his pocket, when he heard children's voices at the rear of the house and paused to round the corner and see what was going on. All Karen saw when she turned, was Stephen standing under the library window, a blade of grass between his teeth and a sneer on his handsome, sullen face.

"Yah!" he jeered: "What'll my mother say *now* when I tell her?"

"Tell her what?" asked Karen, mystified.

"She's always ordering Ginny and me to play with you, 'cause she says you're better brought up than any of the other kids. Just wait till I tell her you play with *niggers!*" He aimed a spit-ball at Joey and disappeared around the corner, yelling at the top of his voice: "Yah! Nigger-lover! Nigger-lover!"

Karen was struck dumb, her cheeks aflame, her whole body quivering. She hid her burning face against the railing of the kitchen porch, her shoulders heaving, her breath coming in gasps. She felt a small hand caressing her arm.

"Don't ya grieve, honey-chile," whispered Joey softly. "I'se used to it—we's *all* used to it." Karen was still silent, still trembling.

"My daddy sez," he went on comfortingly, "folks treats us better up here than down in No'th Ca'lina whar he come from. Down thar, they calls us 'Jim Crow'!"

Karen whirled around, threw her arms about Joey's neck and kissed his brown cheeks, wetting them with her tears.

"Oh, Joey, Joey *dear!*" she wailed.

Then she turned away, dashed up the steps, flung herself through the kitchen door and buried her head, sobbing, in Maggie's capacious lap, as she sat shelling peas beside the kitchen table.

"Sainted glory of the Blessed Virgin! Whatever's got into ye, darlint?" exclaimed Maggie.

Karen was speechless. There were no words for her grief and shame. She could only hide her face in Maggie's apron and sob her heart out.

"Was ye hurted at all?" inquired Maggie, "racin' and rompin' wid that little frisky rascal, Joey?" Karen managed to shake her head.

"Did yez have a fallin'-out wid the young spalpeen?"

"Oh no," sobbed Karen, "Joey never quarrels."

"Wherever is he now at all? Leppin' around outside?"
Karen managed to choke out, "I think he's gone home."

"And whyever wud he be off in such a scorch o' haste?" wondered Maggie. "I saved a bit o' cake for him here, for pickin' me raspberries." No answer from Karen, whose convulsive sobs redoubled.

"Will yez whisht now in a short while," commanded Maggie, "or will I be tellin' herself ye've some sort of a fit taken?" Karen raised an imploring hand.

"Oh, no, no!" she pleaded, between sobs. And then: "Sing—sing to me Maggie dear!"

Maggie gathered the small, tear-stained face close to her ample bosom and began to croon one of her Irish ballads:

"O Paddy dear, and did yez hear the news that's goin' round?
The Shamrock is forbid by law to grow on Irish ground!
No more St. Patrick's Day we'll keep, his color can't be seen,
For there's a cruel law agin the Wearin' o' the Green!

Now, if the color we must wear is England's red,
Let it remoind us of the blood that Ireland has shed;
Then pull the Shamrock from yer hat and t'row it on the sod
An', niver fear, 'twill take root there though underfoot 'tis trod!

When Law can stop the blades of grass from growin' as they
    grow,
An' when the leaves in summer-time their color dare not
    show,
Then I will change the color, too, I wear in my caubeen,
But till that day, plaze God, I'll stick to Wearin' o' the Green!"

Karen could dimly feel that here, too, was something about injustice and unkindness, and though she couldn't understand it, her heart was flooded with an outreaching of pity and sympathy that vaguely comforted her. The throaty voice and the rich flavor of the language held her attention, and the sobs gradually subsided. As the song came to an end she lay quiet in Maggie's warm embrace.

For the time being, Karen was consoled. But from then on, she began to understand what it meant to be a *real* social outcast—to be always an outsider from the beginning to the end of your life. She began to be ashamed of her own self-pity; to try to think, instead, of ways of showing friendship to all the other Joeys, black or brown or yellow, whenever she met them—to try to atone, as far as she could, for some of the hurts they so often had to suffer from an unkind and unjust world.

Down to the bottom of her heart, like a leaden weight, had sunk a phrase that was to echo there and grieve her all through her childhood and, in later years, filling her with personal shame and contrition, to fan a hot flame of social indignation—the phrase, "Jim Crow."

Caroline Foulke Urie

THE BISHOP'S CHAIRS

The Bishop had finished his breakfast. He was ready to begin the day's work. The bacon, the eggs, the buttered toast had all been of the best quality and done to a turn by his excellent cook. The cloth spread on the table was of the whitest linen. As for himself, his hair was smoothly brushed, his gaiters were snug up to his knees, and all his churchly garb was of fine cloth well fitted. The Bishop was not a proud man on his own account, but for the office that he held, of Bishop in the great Church of England, he believed that only the best of everything was good enough.

That was why, when he found that the fine old oak dining-chairs which had come down to him with his palace from the bishop before him, were growing shaky in their joints and worn as to their rungs, he had ordered that the best furniture-maker in the city be called in to look at the chairs and estimate the cost of repairing them; and while he was at it the furniture-maker should also construct six more chairs like the old ones so that the Bishop's hospitable table might have plenty of comfortable chairs for his guests.

And that was why his choice had fallen on a Quaker firm of furniture-makers, said to be the best in the city. A man from the shop had been asked to call directly after the Bishop's breakfast time.

"My lord," said the footman, very neat in his livery of plum-colored coat and knee-breeches, "the man is here to inspect the chairs."

"Very prompt," said the Bishop, approvingly. "I like that. Show him in, Hawkins. Let him measure them while I explain what is wanted."

"Yes, my lord."

The footman bowed and retreated, returning a moment later to announce.

"Mr. John Evans, to measure the chairs, my lord."

There was a disapproving look on his face as he ushered in a young workman in clothing as orderly as that of the Bishop himself, but very plain, and with his broad hat set firmly on his head. He did not bow; his young back was as straight as a tree.

"Well!" thought the Bishop, accustomed to bowing and to bared heads, "Well! So this is a Quaker! I never dealt with one before!" And aloud he said, "Ah! Good morning, Mr. Evans."

"Good morning, friend," the young man said with pleasant gravity.

At this address the Bishop fairly blinked, for even his wife called him my lord, as the title proper for a bishop. Then he thought to himself, "This is a young man of courage. Very unusual!" and to the disapproving footman, lingering in the doorway, he said, "You need not stay, Hawkins."

"Well, my friend," he said to the carpenter, "these are the chairs to be repaired. Can your shop put them in good order and make me a half dozen more like them?"

The young man did not break out in eager promises as the Bishop had fully expected.

"I will see," he said, and very carefully and gently, so as not to loosen the worn joints more, he went over each chair with his long skilful fingers.

When he had carefully examined the worn oak he told the Bishop just what should be done: certain rungs and stretchers must be replaced and all the joints strengthened; the chairs could be copied, certainly, so that the Bishop's dining-table could be extended to its full length.

"And how much will that cost me?" the Bishop asked.

"That I cannot tell thee, friend, until I speak to my employer, who is out of the city but will be coming back today. He can let thee know tomorrow."

"Very well. And I trust," the Bishop said graciously, "that the chairs will be as sturdy and honest as their maker appears to be."

"The chairs will be as good as we can make them," John Evans said quietly, and the Bishop was quite content with this moderate statement.

But when Samuel Hobart, the young man's employer, came back to the shop late that afternoon and heard the report of this visit to the Bishop he was uneasy that all had not been properly done to please this important customer.

"The new Bishop! He is a very particular man, I hear."

"He seemed to know what he wanted," John Evans said tranquilly. "Here are my notes and the measurements of the chairs."

Samuel Hobart hardly looked at them. "I don't doubt that thy measurements are correct. But a Bishop! We never had an order from a Bishop before. I hope thou showed him due courtesy. Why, I would hardly know how to behave toward a Bishop myself!"

John Evans looked down at the anxious little man somewhat pityingly. "I behaved toward him as I would toward thee or any other respectable elderly man."

Samuel Hobart shook his head. "Thou'rt a very 'stiff' Quaker, John Evans. I will visit the Bishop myself in the morning." He thought, "I will see what politeness will do to get me this order. Surely the Bishop must have been offended with John's behavior. John is a very good workman—none better—but he would no more take off his hat to a Bishop than would William Penn himself!"

Next morning, therefore, wearing his very best suit and a ruffled shirt purchased especially for the occasion, he took his estimate and walked to the Bishop's palace, past the imposing cathedral, and all the way he was trying to remember when he should call the Bishop "my lord" and when he should say "your lordship."

He did not go so early as John Evans had called the morning before, because he was afraid that it was not proper to appear so soon, and so it happened that he arrived at the stone steps of the palace at a time when the Bishop was engaged in a conference in his library with some other distinguished gentlemen; but the Bishop remembered John Evans with pleasure and wanted to show him to his friends, and so he ordered that the furniture-maker be shown in at once.

"It will do you good to see a man true to his own conscience," the Bishop told his friends. "I did not, myself, realize how sincerely these Quakers practiced their belief in the equality of men, until this upstanding young carpenter called on me yesterday. No bowing, no titles! He would not flatter me, I believe, even if he thought that by doing so he could sell me a houseful of furniture!"

The little company looked around expectantly as the footman held back the heavy hangings at the door, to see the man so highly praised by their Bishop, and there they saw Samuel Hobart, bowing and scraping his very best, as he had practiced before the mirror the night before. He had by mistake also bowed to the footman at the door and was still somewhat embarrassed by the footman's smile, but he did not mean to let that keep him from making a good impression on the Bishop.

"Er-r, good morning," the Bishop said, surprised at the sight.

"Good morning, my lordship,—your—my lord," Samuel Hobart said, stumbling over the unaccustomed words. "I brought the estimates, my lord, which your lordship kindly asked for yesterday."

There was a little silence in the beautiful room. The furniture-maker lifted his bobbing head and looked around. He wondered if, after all, in his Quakerly ignorance, he had not been mannerly enough. Perhaps all of these other gentlemen were lords also, and should be addressed by title.

"You aren't the same man that came yesterday," said the Bishop, much displeased.

"Oh no," said Samuel Hobart. He decided that the Bishop must still be offended at John Evans' behavior. "Oh no, my lordship. That was a worthy young man, who is an excellent carpenter, but with no experience in dealing with customers of rank."

"But aren't you both Quakers?" The Bishop's tone was still sharp.

"Yes, my lord." Samuel Hobart began to feel very uncomfortable.

"Put the estimates on the table," the Bishop ordered. He felt that his friends were smiling at his discomfiture. "I have important matters to occupy me now. Tomorrow you may send up the young man who came first. I prefer to deal with him."

Without a word Samuel Hobart laid the paper on the table and turned to leave the scene of his hopes, and the kind-hearted Bishop, seeing his unhappiness, relented a little.

"Hark you, my friend," he said. "Let a man of experience give you a few words of advice. Don't be ashamed of carrying out your own religion, whether you are in a carpenter's shop or in a Bishop's palace. My religion differs in its observances from your young carpenter's, but I admire him for holding to his sincere convictions."

He looked around the little circle for approval and all the other gentlemen nodded agreement.

"And now, good-bye, friend."

"Farewell my—friend," said the furniture-maker, and he walked out past the haughty footman, blushing but with his head up.

THE SERMON
IN THE WILDERNESS

ⲧⲧⲧ

"My friend, I have explained that I must have the horse, and that I will deposit with thee his full value until his safe return within a week's time."

The tall man spoke a trifle wearily, as though he had had almost enough of the argument. It was a hot day on the edge of the great Pennsylvania forest. The dust in front of the Rockville tavern still hung in a cloud where the coach, on its weekly arrival from the distant city, had stirred it a-fresh. The group of farmers, waiting for mail and news of the outside world, had watched with curious eyes this stranger descend from the high seat beside the driver. They had noted the broad-brimmed hat, white stock, carpet bag and closely fitting "store" clothes that marked him as city-bred, and the foreign way he used his hands when he talked. Their natural distrust had melted, however, before the radiant smile of more than ordinary good-will that lighted up the blue eyes and wrinkled the lean face as he strode briskly toward them crying, "The peace of God be with you, my friends! From which of you may I obtain a horse for a journey into the wilderness?"

Several minutes of parley followed between the innkeeper and the stranger, not a word being lost by the eager group of listeners. This man insisted that he must travel for three days straight into the heart of the forest "along a way that would be opened" to him. The innkeeper objected that there was only one trail a horse could travel, and this exceedingly dangerous, with treacherous fords and rocky pitfalls. Did the stranger know that the three-days' trail led only to a lumber camp, and that honest men who valued their lives or their purses did well to avoid this place? Adventurous explorers had been known to enter the dark forest, never to return. Was the gentleman's business so imperative that he would risk his life?

"It is my Father's business, and the most imperative in the world," answered the stranger calmly. "Should a hundred men beset my path, I should go unharmed. I have received instructions from Above and go without fear, for the Spirit upholds me. So, if I may hire a horse of thee——"

At length a wiry little mare was brought out and a dozen hands helped saddle her. The stranger, though urged to remain over night, refused courteously, explaining that he carried food and was accustomed to sleep in the open. As he paid for the mare and was about to ride away, the innkeeper inquired, "What is your name, stranger?"

"Stephen Grellet, of New York, and I go to carry the message of God to those who will listen."

As the little mare and the man climbed the rough path and disappeared into the birches that edged the dark pines, one man remarked, "A Quaker, I know by his speech, and a godly man. But he cannot melt the hearts of those men with his soft tongue."

Stephen Grellet found a single trail winding now along the slippery banks of a rushing stream, now over treacherous moss-covered rocks, skirting steep cliffs, and twice plunging through the river where the mare was forced to swim. During the first afternoon he passed several clearings with little cabins, where children ran out to wave and call to him; but after this he saw no work of human hands except the logs left by receding spring floods along the banks. Though no sounds except those of the forest came to his ears, he moved with a radiance in his eyes and with a smile upon his lips, as though he were listening to the cheery words of a dear companion.

Early in the afternoon of the third day—a breathless day, when even the birds were voiceless and the low, pulsing drone of insects made the silence seem only more profound —Stephen Grellet found the trail widened into a corduroy road where horses had evidently been used to drag the logs down to the river bank. He noticed a pile of rusty cans and a piece of chain hanging on a branch. Then rounding a huge rock, Stephen suddenly found himself on the edge of a space from which all trees and underbrush had been cleared. Facing him on the far side stood a large three-sided log shed; to the left and right of this shed were several rough, closed cabins, the bark from their slab sides hanging in tatters. A pile of black embers in the center of the space added a last touch of desolation.

Stephen Grellet reined in his mare in great perplexity. The message that had come to him had been very clear, and as was the habit of his life, he had followed the leading of the Spirit in perfect faith. He knew that he was to come to this spot in the heart of the wilderness where a gang of wood-cutters, far-famed for their lawlessness, had been operating, and here he was to preach the simple and holy truth of God's presence in the forest. It had not once occurred to him that, as evidently was the case, the lumbermen might have moved on deeper into the forest. He knew without question, however, that this was the place where he must preach. Alighting, he tied his mare to a sapling, leaving her to browse the long wood grass, and made his way to the central cabin where rough tables stood on a slightly raised floor. Mounting this platform, he faced the forest, a strange inner light making his face glow. During his long life he had traveled to the far corners of the earth, defying dangers and discomforts in order to carry the simple assurance of God's love to all people; yet never had he felt more completely the Divine Presence flooding through and around his whole being than when now he stood alone in the deserted camp, surrounded by the mystery of the forest. The afternoon sun, slanting between the brown tree pillars, fell upon a gold-green mass of ferns at his feet, and the fronds quivered, stirred by some tiny wood beast scampering through the stems.

"Oh, God—thou art here—here!" he cried, stretching wide his arms. As if in answer, a low murmur breathed in the tree-tops, swelling nearer, moving the pine needles softly. Then a loud rustle, perhaps of a startled animal behind the cabin, gave Stephen Grellet the sense that all around him were the invisible eyes and ears of the forest folk. To them and to God he spoke aloud, his words, blending the faith and joy of his own soul with the dignity of the pines, the grace of the fern fronds, the vitality of the little scurrying beasts, and over all the softly moving Presence in the wind-stirred branches.

At last, silent, with head bowed, he heard far off the leisurely, bell-like notes of the thrush thrilling through the forest spaces. With infinite peace in his heart he mounted the little mare and rode away, back to Rockville and the world.

*   *   *

Six years later Stephen Grellet was in London. He had gone there, as he had gone into the forests of Pennsylvania, guided only by the Spirit. He had gone down into the narrow, filthy streets, where men and women seemed too sodden to understand when he told them of the love of the Father, and he had preached in dark prisons where men looked at him dully when he spoke of the Divine Light. Yet whenever he ceased speaking there were always some who crowded nearer, seeking to know more of this Being who had sent him to show them the way out of their wretchedness.

Late one afternoon, smothered by the stagnant air of the slums, he walked on London Bridge as the setting sun was throwing a broken red path on the oily water of the Thames. He was very tired, for he threw all his strength into the struggle to show to others the Light that burned in his own soul. As he stood looking at the spires of the vast city against the glow of the evening sky, he prayed for faith and peace. Suddenly the roar of London died in his ears and he heard again the gentle sighing of the pines in the Pennsylvania forest and the clear notes of the thrush. Just as truly God was with him here—

The revery of Stephen Grellet was shattered by someone seizing him roughly by the elbow. He turned quickly to face a broad, muscular man, with rugged face and eyes of piercing eagerness, who cried, in great excitement, as he peered into Stephen Grellet's face, "I have got you at last! I have got you at last!"

Stephen returned the gaze calmly, but could see nothing familiar about the man except that he was certainly an American.

"Friend," he replied, "I think thou art mistaken."

"But I am not—I cannot be! I have carried every line of your face in my memory for six years. How I have longed to see it again!"

"Who, then, art thou, and where dost thou think we have met?" inquired Stephen.

"Did you not preach in the great forest of Pennsylvania, three days' trip from the village of Rockville, six years ago last midsummer?"

"I did, but I saw no one there to listen."

The man held out his hands to Stephen Grellet—strong

hands that had known hard toil. "I was there," he replied, his voice full of awe as the memory rose again before him. "I was the head of the woodmen who had deserted those shanties. We had moved on into the forest and were putting up more cabins to live in, when I discovered that I had left my lever at the old settlement. So, leaving my men at work, I went back alone for my tool. As I approached the old place I heard a voice. Trembling and agitated, I drew near, and saw you through the chinks in the timber walls of our dining shanty. I listened to you, and something in your face or in your words, or both, stirred me as I had never been stirred before. I went back to my men. I was miserable for weeks; I had no Bible, no book of any kind, no one to speak to about divine things.

"At last I found the strength I needed. I obtained a Bible; I told my men the blessed news that God was near us, and we learned together to ask forgiveness and to lead better lives. Three of us became missionaries and went forth to tell thousands of others of the joy and faith you brought into the forest."

NOT LOST, BUT GONE BEFORE

"WHERE do you suppose he went?" inquired the Dragon-fly Grub as he watched the Frog swim to the top of the pond and suddenly disappear.

"I don't know and I don't care," replied a saucy Minnow whose whole object in life was getting enough to eat and having a good time.

The poor little Grub looked crest-fallen. He had spent a great deal of time pondering on this subject and he could not understand why his companions were not equally curious.

"Why don't you ask him when he comes back?" suggested an elderly Eel who had been listening to the conversation.

Now in the pond world the Frog is a very important and dignified personage and the little Grub had never been able to muster up courage to speak to him. But today, he determined to be very brave. He waited patiently until—splash— there was a great disturbance and the Frog came swimming back.

"Mr. Frog, please, Mr. Frog," called the Grub, "there is something I *must* ask you."

The Frog stopped swimming and turned his great goggle eyes in the direction of the Grub. "Indeed," said he, "Proceed!"

"Mr. Frog, what is there beyond the world?" stammered the Grub, so scared he could scarcely speak.

"What world do you mean?" inquired the Frog.

"*This* world, of course—our world," answered the Grub.

"This *pond*, you mean," sneered the Frog.

"I mean the place we live in, whatever you may choose to call it," cried the Grub. "I call it the world."

"Oh, do you?" rejoined the Frog. "Well, then, what do you call the place you don't live in, up there beyond your world, eh?"

"That's just what I'm asking you," retorted the Grub.

"Well, I'll tell you," said the Frog in his most pompous manner. "It's dry land."

"But what's dry land?"

The poor Frog was really nonplussed, for he did not know how to answer. So he said in a very condescending manner, "Of all the inquisitive creatures I ever met, you certainly are the most troublesome. Dry land is something like the mud at the bottom of this pond, only it isn't wet, because there isn't any water."

"No water!" interrupted the Grub. "Well, what is there then?"

"They call it air," said the Frog, "and if you've never been there, I can't make you understand what it's like. It's more like *nothing* than anything else."

The poor little Grub was more confused than ever and he looked so downcast that the Frog took pity on him and said, "You are a very silly fellow not to be satisfied with the experience of others. But as I rather admire your spirit, I will make you an offer. If you choose to take a seat on my back, I will carry you up to dry land and let you see for yourself what it's like."

The Grub climbed joyfully on the Frog's back and the Frog swam gently upward till he reached the bulrushes by the water's side.

"Hold fast," cried the Frog as he clambered up on the bank and got upon the grass.

"Now, then, here we are!" exclaimed he. "What do you think of dry land?"

But no one spoke in reply.

"Halloo! gone?" he continued; "that's just what I was afraid of. Perhaps he'll climb up by himself. I'll wait here and see."

But the Grub, meanwhile? The moment he reached the surface of the water a terrible sensation had come over him and he reeled off the Frog's back, panting and struggling for life. It was several seconds before he recovered himself.

"Horrible," cried he when he got his wits together. "Beyond this world there is nothing but Death. Mr. Frog has deceived me."

He contented himself for the present therefore, with telling his friends what he had done, and where he had been. Now that he had really had a thrilling experience he found a great many eager to hear about it.

That evening, as the Grub was returning from a ramble among the water plants, he suddenly encountered his friend, the yellow Frog.

"You here!" cried the startled Grub, and was about to tell the Frog what he thought of him for deceiving him about the World Beyond when the Frog interrupted with, "Why didn't you sit fast as I told you?"

They would soon have had a serious quarrel if the Frog had not suggested that the Grub tell his story and show why he had been so clumsy as to fall off.

The story was soon told. "And, now," said the Grub in conclusion, "as it is certain there is nothing beyond this world but Death, all of your stories about going there were not true. You evidently don't care to say where you do go. I will, therefore, bid you a very good evening."

"You will do no such thing till you have listened as patiently to my story as I have to yours," exclaimed the Frog.

Then the Frog told how he had waited for the Grub and

"At last," he continued, "though I didn't see you, I saw a sight which will interest you more than any creature that lives. Up the stalk of one of those bulrushes, I saw a Grub just like you slowly climbing until he had left the water, and was clinging to the stem in the full glare of the sun. I must say I was surprised, knowing how fond you all are of the shady bottom of the pond. So I stayed and watched and then a very wonderful thing happened—a rent seemed to come in your friend's body and gradually after much squirming and struggling there came out from it a glorious Dragon-fly. Oh, little Grub, you who have never seen the sunshine and who have lived here in the ugly mud of this dark pond can not imagine what a beautiful creature a Dragon-fly is. It has wonderful, gauzy wings and its body gives out rays of glittering blue and green. I watched it fly in great circles and then I plunged below to tell you the splendid news."

"It is a wonderful story," said the Grub—"but"—and, then, he began to wonder whether it could really be true and whether perhaps it might some day happen to him.

Weeks passed and the Grub often thought of what the Frog had told him. Finally one day he felt sick and weak and had an overwhelming desire to go upwards. The other grubs gathered around him and made him promise that if indeed the wonderful change should happen to him, he would return and tell them so. He promised and then slowly climbed up the bulrush stalk. A few of his friends and relatives went near the surface of the water hoping to see what happened but alas! their eyes were made to see only in the water, and as soon as the Grub reached the air, he was lost to their sight.

And then the wonderful change did take place. The Grub burst his shell and became a beautiful Dragon-fly. At last his hopes had come true.

Did he forget his promise to go back and tell his comrades? No, indeed, he did not forget, but when he tried to descend into the water he had the same sensation as before, when a Grub, he had tried to come out into the air. But although he could not go back to them, he often flew close to the surface of the pond, longing to be able to tell his comrades of the great joy that was in store for them.

Adapted from Parables From Nature *by Mrs. Alfred Gatty.*

THE GREAT STONE FACE

ONE afternoon when the sun was going down, a mother and her little boy sat at the door of their cottage, talking about the Great Stone Face. They had but to lift their eyes, and there it was plainly to be seen, though miles away, with the sunshine brightening all its features.

And what was the Great Stone Face?

The Great Stone Face was a work of Nature in her mood of majestic playfulness, formed on the perpendicular side of a mountain by some immense rocks, which had been thrown together in such a position as, when viewed at a proper distance, precisely to resemble the features of a human countenance. It seemed as if an enormous giant, or a Titan, had sculptured his own likeness on the precipice. There was the broad arch of the forehead, a hundred feet in height; the nose, with its long bridge; and the vast lips, which, if they could have spoken, would have rolled their thunder accents from one end of the valley to the other. True it is, that if the spectator approached too near, he lost the outline of the gigantic visage, and could discern only a heap of ponderous and gigantic rocks, piled in chaotic ruin one upon another. Retracing his steps, however, the wondrous features would again be seen; and the farther he withdrew from them, the more like a human face, with all its original dignity intact, did they appear; until, as it grew dim in the distance, with the clouds and glorified vapor of the mountains clustering about it, the Great Stone Face seemed positively to be alive.

As we began with saying, a mother and her little boy sat at their cottage door, gazing at the Great Stone Face, and talking about it. The child's name was Ernest.

"Mother, said he, while the Titanic visage smiled on him, "I wish that it could speak, for it looks so very kindly that its voice must needs be pleasant. If I were to see a man with such a face, I should love him dearly."

"If an old prophecy should come to pass," answered his mother, "we may see a man, some time or other, with exactly such a face as that."

And then his mother told him a story that her own mother had told to her, when she herself was younger than little Ernest; a story, not of things that were past, but of what was yet to come; a story, nevertheless, so very old, that even the Indians who formerly inhabited this valley, had heard it from their forefathers, to whom, as they affirmed, it had been murmured by the mountain streams, and whispered by the wind among the tree-tops. The purport was, that, at some future day, a child should be born hereabouts, who was destined to become the greatest and noblest personage of his time, and whose countenance, in manhood, should bear an exact resemblance to the Great Stone Face. Not a few old-fashioned people, and young ones likewise, still cherished an enduring faith in this old prophecy. But others, who had seen more of the world, had watched and waited till they were weary and had beheld no man with such a face, concluded it to be nothing but an idle tale.

Ernest never forgot the story. It was in his mind, whenever he looked upon the Great Stone Face. He spent his childhood in the log-cottage where he was born. From a happy, yet often pensive child, he grew up to be a mild, quiet, unobtrusive boy. When the toil of the day was over, he would gaze for hours at the Great Stone Face until he began to imagine that those vast features recognized him, and gave him a smile of kindness and encouragement. We must not take upon us to affirm that this was a mistake, although the Face may have looked no more kindly at Ernest than at all the world beside. But the secret was, that the boy's tender and confiding simplicity discerned what other people could not see; and thus the love, which was meant for all, became his peculiar portion.

About this time, there went a rumor throughout the valley, that the great man, foretold from ages long ago, who was to bear a resemblance to the Great Stone Face had appeared at last. It seems that, many years before, a young man had migrated from the valley and settled at a distant seaport, where, after getting together a little money, he had set up as a shopkeeper. His name—but I could never learn whether it was his real one, or a nickname that had grown out of his habits and success in life—was Gathergold. It might be said of him, as of Midas in the fable, that whatever he touched with his fingers immediately glistened and was changed into sterling metal, or, which suited him still better, into piles of coin. And when Mr. Gathergold had become so very rich, he bethought himself of his native valley, and resolved to go back thither, and end his days where he was born. With this purpose in view, he sent a skilful architect to build him such a palace as should be fit for a man of his vast wealth to live in.

As I have said, it had already been rumored in the valley that Mr. Gathergold had turned out to be the prophetic personage and that his visage was the perfect and undeniable similitude of the Great Stone Face. People were the more ready to believe that this must needs be the fact, when they beheld the splendid marble edifice that rose, as if by enchantment, on the site of his father's old weatherbeaten farm-house.

Ernest had been deeply stirred by the idea that the great man, the noble man, the man of prophecy, after so many ages of delay, was at length to be made manifest to his

native valley. He knew, boy as he was, that there were a
thousand ways in which Mr. Gathergold with his vast
wealth might assume a control over human affairs as wide
and benignant as the smile of the Great Stone Face. Full
of faith and hope, Ernest doubted not that what the people
said was true, and that now he was to behold the living
likeness of those wondrous features on the mountainside.
While the boy was gazing up the valley, and fancying, as
he always did, that the Great Stone Face returned his gaze
and looked kindly at him, the rumbling of wheels was
heard, approaching swiftly along the winding road.

"Here he comes!" cried a group of people who were assembled to witness the arrival. "Here comes the great Mr.
Gathergold!"

A carriage, drawn by four horses, dashed round the turn
of the road. Within it, thrust partly out of the window,
appeared the physiognomy of a little old man with yellow
skin, a low forehead, small, sharp eyes, puckered about
with innumerable wrinkles, and very thin lips which he
made still thinner by pressing them forcibly together.

"The very image of the Great Stone Face!" shouted the
people. "Sure enough, the old prophecy is true; and here
we have the great man come, at last."

And what greatly perplexed Ernest, they seemed actually
to believe that here was the likeness which they spoke of.

Ernest turned sadly from the wrinkled shrewdness of
that sordid visage, and gazed up the valley, where, amid a
gathering mist, gilded by the last sunbeams, he could dis-
tinguish those glorious features which had impressed themselves into his soul. Their aspect cheered him. What did
the benign lips seem to say?

"He will come! Fear not, Ernest; the man will come!"

The years went on and Ernest ceased to be a boy. He
had grown to be a young man now. He attracted little

notice from the inhabitants of the valley; for they saw nothing remarkable in his way of life, save that, when the labor of the day was over, he still loved to go apart and gaze and meditate upon the Great Stone Face.

By this time poor Mr. Gathergold was dead. His wealth, which was the body and spirit of his existence, had disappeared before his death, leaving nothing of him but a living skeleton, covered over with a wrinkled yellow skin. Since the melting away of his gold, it had been very generally conceded that there was no such striking resemblance, after all, betwixt the ignoble features of the ruined merchant and that majestic face upon the mountain-side. The man of prophecy was yet to come.

It so happened that a native-born son of the valley, many years before, had enlisted as a soldier, and, after a great deal of hard fighting, had now become an illustrious commander. Whatever he may be called in history, he was known in camps, and on the battle-field under the nickname of Old Blood-and-Thunder. This war-worn veteran had lately signified a purpose of returning to his native valley, hoping to find repose where he remembered to have left it. The inhabitants were resolved to welcome the renowned warrior with a salute of cannon and a public dinner; and all the more enthusiastically, it being affirmed that now, at last, the likeness of the Great Stone Face had actually appeared.

On the great day of the festival, Ernest, with all the other people of the valley, left their work, and proceeded to the spot where the sylvan banquet was prepared. Ernest, being of an unobtrusive character, was thrust quite into the background, where he could see no more of Old Blood-and-Thunder's physiognomy than if it had been still blazing on the battle-field. To console himself, he turned towards the Great Stone Face, which, like a faithful and long-remembered friend, looked back and smiled upon him through the vista of the forest. Meantime, however, he could overhear the remarks of various individuals, who were comparing the features of the hero with the face on the distant mountain-side.

"'Tis the same face, to a hair!" cried one man, cutting a caper for joy.

"Wonderfully like, that's a fact!" responded another.

"Like! why I call it Old Blood-and-Thunder himself, in a monstrous looking-glass!" cried a third.

And then all three gave a great shout which communicated electricity to the crowd, and called forth a roar from a thousand voices that went reverberating for miles among the mountains.

"The General! the General!" was now the cry.

The General now stood upon his feet to thank the company and Ernest saw him. There he was over the shoulders of the crowd, from the glittering epaulets and embroidered collar upward, beneath the arch of the green boughs with intertwined laurel. And there, too, visible in the same glance, through the vista of the forest, appeared the Great Stone Face. And was there, indeed, such a resemblance as the crowd had testified? Alas, Ernest could not recognize it! He beheld a war-torn and weather-beaten countenance, full of energy, and expressive of an iron will; but the gentle wisdom, the deep, broad tender sympathies, were altogether wanting in Old Blood-and-Thunder's visage.

"This is not the man of prophecy," sighed Ernest to himself as he made his way out of the throng.

The mists had congregated about the distant mountain-side, and there were seen the grand and awful features of the Great Stone Face, awful but benignant, as if a mighty angel were sitting among the hills and enrobing himself in a cloud-vesture of gold and purple.

"Fear not, Ernest," said his heart, even as if the Great Face were whispering him,—"fear not, Ernest; he will come."

More years sped swiftly and tranquilly away; Ernest still dwelt in his native valley, and was now a man of middle age. By imperceptible degrees, he had become known among the people. Now, as heretofore, he labored for his bread, and was the same simple-hearted man he had always been. But he had thought and felt so much, he had given so many of the best years of his life to unworldly hopes for some great good to mankind, that it seemed as though he had been talking with the angels, and had imbibed a portion of their wisdom unawares. It was visible in the calm and well-considered beneficence of his daily life, the quiet stream of which had made a wide green margin all along its course. Not a day passed by, that the world was not the better because this man, humble as he was, had lived. He never stepped aside from his own path, yet would always reach a blessing to his neighbor. Almost involuntarily, too, he had become a preacher. The pure and high simplicity of his thought, which as one of its manifestations, took shape in the good deeds that dropped silently from his hand, flowed also forth in speech. He uttered truths that wrought upon and moulded the lives of those who heard him. His auditors, it may be, never suspected that Ernest, their own neighbor and familiar friend, was more than an ordinary man; least of all did Ernest himself suspect it.

Now again there were reports and many paragraphs in the newspapers, affirming that the likeness of the Great Stone Face had appeared upon the broad shoulders of a certain eminent statesman. He, like Mr. Gathergold and old Blood-and-Thunder, was a native of the valley, but had left it in his early days, and taken up the trades of law and politics. Instead of the rich man's wealth and the warrior's sword, he had but a tongue, and it was mightier than both together. So wonderfully eloquent was he, that whatever he might choose to say, his auditors had no choice but to believe him, he could make a kind of illuminated fog with his mere breath, and obscure the natural daylight with it. He was a wondrous man; and when his tongue had acquired him all other imaginable success it finally persuaded his countrymen to select him for the Presidency. Before this time—indeed, as soon as he began to grow celebrated—his admirers had found out the resemblance between him and the Great Stone Face; and so much were they struck with it that throughout the country this distinguished gentleman was known by the name of Old Stony Phiz.

While his friends were doing their best to make him President, Old Stony Phiz set out on a visit to the valley where he was born. Magnificent preparations were made to receive the illustrious statesman; a cavalcade of horsemen set forth to meet him at the boundary line of the State, and all the people left their business and gathered along the wayside to see him pass. Among these was Ernest. Though more than once disappointed, as we have seen, he had such a hopeful and confiding nature, that he was always ready to believe in whatever seemed beautiful and good. So now again, as buoyantly as ever, he went forth to behold the likeness of the Great Stone Face.

The cavalcade came prancing along the road, with a great clattering of hoofs and a mighty cloud of dust, which rose up so dense and high that the visage of the mountain-side was completely hidden from Ernest's eyes. All the great men of the neighborhood were there on horseback. It really was a very brilliant spectacle, especially as there were numerous banners on some of which were gorgeous portraits of the illustrious statesman and the Great Stone Face, smiling familiarly at one another, like two brothers. If the pictures were to be trusted, the mutual resemblance, it must be confessed, was marvelous.

In the midst of all this gallant array, came an open barouche, drawn by four white horses; and in the barouche, with his massive head uncovered, sat Old Stony Phiz himself.

"Confess it," said one of Ernest's neighbors to him, "the Great Stone Face has met its match at last!"

Now it must be owned that, at his first glimpse of the countenance which was bowing and smiling from the barouche, Ernest did fancy that there was a resemblance between it and the old familiar face upon the mountainside. The brow, with its massive depth and loftiness, and all the other features, indeed, were boldly and strongly hewn, as if in emulation of a more than heroic, of a Titanic model. But the sublimity and stateliness, the grand expression of a divine sympathy, that illuminated the mountain visage, and etherealized its ponderous granite substance into spirit, might here be sought in vain. Something had been originally left out, or had departed. And therefore the marvelously gifted statesman had always a weary gloom in the deep caverns of his eyes, as of a child that has outgrown its playthings, or a man of mighty faculties and little aims, whose life with all its high performances, was vague and empty, because no high purpose had endowed it with reality.

Still Ernest's neighbor was thrusting his elbow into his side, and pressing him for an answer.

"Confess! Confess! Is not he the very picture of your Old Man of the Mountain?"

"No!" said Ernest, bluntly, "I see little or no likeness."

"Then so much the worse for the Great Stone Face!"

answered his neighbor; and again he set up a shout for Old Stony Phiz.

But Ernest turned away, melancholy, for this was the saddest of his disappointments: to behold a man who might have fulfilled the prophecy and had not willed to do so. Meantime the cavalcade swept past him leaving the dust to settle down, and the Great Stone Face to be revealed again, with the grandeur it had worn for untold centuries.

"Lo, here I am, Ernest!" the benign lips seemed to say. "I have waited longer than thou, and am not yet weary. Fear not; the man will come.

The years hurried onward, treading in their haste on one another's heels. Ernest was an aged man. But not in vain had he grown old: more than the white hairs on his head were the sage thoughts in his mind. Ernest had ceased to be obscure. Unsought for, undesired, had come the fame which so many seek, and made him known in the great world, beyond the limits of the valley in which he had dwelt so quietly. Whether it were sage, statesman, or philanthropist, Ernest received all visitors with the gentle sincerity that had characterized him from boyhood, and spoke freely with them of whatever came uppermost, or lay deepest in his heart or their own. While they talked together, his face would kindle, unawares, and shine upon them, as with a mild evening light. Pensive with the fulness of such discourse, his guests took leave and went their way; and passing up the valley, paused to look at the Great Stone Face, imagining that they had seen its likeness in human countenance, but could not remember where.

While Ernest had been growing up and growing old, a bountiful Providence had granted a new poet to this earth. He, likewise, was a native of the valley, but had spent the greater part of his life at a distance from that romantic region, pouring out his sweet music amid the bustle and din of cities.

The songs of this poet found their way to Ernest. He read them after his customary toil, seated on the bench before his cottage-door, where for such a length of time he had filled his repose with thought, by gazing at the Great Stone Face. And now as he read stanzas that caused the soul to thrill within him, he lifted his eyes to the vast countenance beaming on him so benignantly.

"O majestic friend," he murmured, addressing the Great Stone Face, "is not this man worthy to resemble thee?"

Now it happened that the poet, though he dwelt so far away, had not only heard of Ernest, but had meditated much upon his character, until he deemed nothing so desirable as to meet this man, whose untaught wisdom walked hand in hand with the noble simplicity of his life. One summer morning, therefore, he took passage by railroad, and, in the decline of the afternoon, alighted from the cars at no great distance from Ernest's cottage. The great hotel, which had formerly been the palace of Mr. Gathergold, was close at hand, but the poet, with his carpet-bag on his arm, inquired at once where Ernest dwelt, and was resolved to be accepted as his guest.

Approaching the door, he there found the good old man, holding a volume in his hand, which alternately he read, and then, with a finger between the leaves, looked lovingly at the Great Stone Face.

"Good evening," said the poet. "Can you give a traveler a night's lodging?"

"Willingly," answered Ernest; and then he added smiling, "Methinks I never saw the Great Stone Face look so hospitably at a stranger."

The poet sat down on the bench beside him, and he and Ernest talked together.

As Ernest listened to the poet, he imagined that the Great Stone Face was bending forward to listen too. He gazed earnestly into the poet's eyes.

"Who are you, my strangely gifted guest?" he said.

The poet laid his finger on the volume that Ernest had been reading.

"You have read these poems," he said. "You know me then,—for I wrote them."

Again, and still more earnestly than before, Ernest examined the poet's features; then turned towards the Great Stone Face; then back, with an uncertain aspect, to his guest. But his countenance fell; he shook his head and sighed.

"Wherefore, are you sad?" inquired the poet.

"Because," replied Ernest, "all through life I have awaited the fulfillment of a prophecy; and when I read these poems, I hoped that it might be fulfilled in you."

"You hoped," answered the poet, faintly smiling, "to find in me the likeness of the Great Stone Face. And you are disappointed, as formerly with Mr. Gathergold, and Old Blood-and-Thunder, and Old Stony Phiz. Yes, Ernest, it is my doom. You must add my name to the illustrious three and record another failure of your hopes. For—in shame and sadness do I speak it, Ernest—I am not worthy to be typified by yonder benign and majestic image."

"And why?" asked Ernest. He pointed to the volume. "Are not these thoughts divine?"

"They have a strain of the Divinity," replied the poet. "You can hear in them the far-off echo of a heavenly song. But my life, dear Ernest, has not corresponded with my thought. I have lived—and that, too, by my own choice— among poor and mean realities. Why, then, pure seeker of the good and true, shouldst thou hope to find me in yonder image of the divine?"

The poet spoke sadly, and his eyes were dim with tears. So, likewise, were those of Ernest.

At the hour of sunset, as had long been his frequent custom, Ernest was to discourse to an assemblage of the neighboring inhabitants in the open air. He and the poet, arm in arm, still talking together as they went along, proceeded to the spot. It was a small nook among the hills. At a small elevation above the ground, there appeared a niche spacious enough to admit a human figure. Into this natural pulpit Ernest ascended, and threw a look of familiar kindness around upon his audience. They stood, or sat, or reclined upon the grass, as seemed good to each, with the departing sunshine falling obliquely over them.

Ernest began to speak, giving to the people of what was in his heart and mind. His words had power, because they accorded with his thoughts; and his thoughts had reality and depth because they harmonized with the life he had lived. It was not mere breath that this preacher uttered; they were the words of life, because a life of good deeds and holy love was melted into them. The poet, as he listened, felt that the being and character of Ernest were a nobler strain of poetry than he had ever written. His eyes glistening with tears, he gazed reverentially at the venerable man, and said within himself that never was there an aspect so worthy of a prophet and a sage as that mild, sweet, thoughtful countenance, with the glory of white hair diffused about it. At a distance, but distinctly to be seen, high up in the golden light of the setting sun, appeared the Great Stone Face, with hoary mists around it, like the white hairs around the brow of Ernest. Its look of grand benevolence seemed to embrace the world.

At that moment, in sympathy with a thought which he was about to utter, the face of Ernest assumed a grandeur of expression, so imbued with benevolence, that the poet, by an irresistible impulse, threw his arms aloft, and shouted,—

"Behold! Behold! Ernest is himself the likeness of the Great Stone Face!"

Then all the people looked, and saw that what the deep-sighted poet said was true. The prophecy was fulfilled. But Ernest, having finished what he had to say, took the poet's arm, and walked slowly homeward, still hoping that some wiser and better man than himself would by and by appear, bearing a resemblance to the Great Stone Face.

Abridged from The Snow Image and Other Twice Told Tales *by Nathaniel Hawthorne*